Rethinking
DARWIN

Rethinking
DARWIN

*A Vedic Study of Darwinism
and Intelligent Design*

LEIF A. JENSEN

with chapters contributed by

**Jonathan Wells, William A. Dembski,
Michael J. Behe, and Michael A. Cremo**

THE BHAKTIVEDANTA BOOK TRUST

For more information please contact

rethinking.darwin@bbt.se

www.krishna.com

ISBN 978-91-7149-568-6

Printed in Germany 2010

Contents

Introduction

"No biologist has been responsible for more – and for more drastic – modifications of the average person's worldview than Charles Darwin."[1]

These words were spoken by Harvard professor Ernst Mayr (1904–2005), veteran evolutionary biologist, when on September 23, 1999, he received the Crafoord Prize from the Royal Swedish Academy of Sciences in Stockholm. Dr. Mayr made the point that although most groundbreaking scientists, such as Albert Einstein, had a marked influence within their own fields of science, they made little impact on the way the average person apprehends the world, whereas Darwin changed the very fabric of our worldview.

And so this book. As long as the ideas of Darwin are so deeply woven into the lives of almost everyone, they will continue to be explored, explained, and critiqued from different perspectives. This book presents an overall scientific critique of Darwin's theory of evolution in a way that is accessible to laypersons, contains novel material and new perspectives that may interest even insiders within the scientific community, and offers an alternative viewpoint to standard modern evolutionary thinking.

One distinguishing feature of this book is that it is written from the standpoint of someone trained in the thoughts of Eastern philosophy, or, more precisely, in the Vedic tradition of ancient India. This natu-

rally has a bearing on the material selected and the issues discussed in the book, and the last chapter directly outlines a Vedic philosophy of nature as an alternative to Darwinism.

Not only is this book about evolution; it is also, in its own right, the result of an evolution. It started as an idea to present some Vedic perspectives on Darwinism in the form of an easy-to-read booklet, to be published and widely distributed during the Darwin bicentennial in 2009. As the material accumulated, I saw that more than a small publication was tak-

Charles Darwin (1809–1882)

ing shape. At one point I contacted three of the world's leading proponents of Intelligent Design, professor of biochemistry Dr. Michael Behe, mathematician and philosopher Dr. William A. Dembski, and biologist Dr. Jonathan Wells. They all found the idea of a book with a Vedic angle an interesting challenge, and each agreed to contribute a chapter. Then historian of archeology Dr. Michael Cremo, co-author of the taboo-breaking book *Forbidden Archeology* – a work directly inspired by the Vedic account of a human presence in ancient times – also consented to write a chapter. Clearly, a unique publication was unfolding. The result is what you now hold in your hand.

Until Darwin's time, mainstream science had concluded that life was too intricate to have been caused by nature alone. Almost a hundred years before Darwin, when the Swedish botanist Carolus Linnaeus (1707–1778) revolutionized biology by inventing the system of taxonomy we still use today, he created a nested hierarchy showing all living forms as related, classifying them by species, genus, family (order), class, and kingdom. This didn't mean Linnaeus read natural evolution into his biological hierarchy; like almost any other scientist of his day, he saw the hierarchy as the materialization of a divine plan.

This view changed when Darwin, in 1859, published *On the Origin of Species*. Within Darwin's lifetime – perhaps only two decades after *Origin* was published – almost the only way a scientist could think and still be respected was as a natural evolutionist. This does not mean Darwin's ideas went uncontested. Many leading scientists of his day found evolution unconvincing. But the tide in favor of the theory was so strong that even Harvard professor Louis Agassiz, one of the nineteenth century's most stalwart natural scientists, fell practically into obscurity because of his opposition to Darwinian thought.

In the words of biologist Francisco Ayala, former president of the American Association for the Advancement of Science:

> Darwin's greatest accomplishment was to show that the complex order and function in living creatures can be explained as a result of a natural process – natural selection – without having to refer to a Creator or some other external factor.[2]

British zoologist Richard Dawkins put the matter more bluntly: "Darwin made it possible to be an intellectually fulfilled atheist."[3]

Of course, whether creating atheists was Darwin's actual intent is uncertain, even unlikely. At least in *Origin*, he only argued that the numerous species of living organisms need not have been created separately but could have emerged naturally, on their own, over eons, from one or a few simple and original life forms ("I view all beings not as special creations, but as the lineal descendants of some few beings which lived long before the first bed of the Silurian system was deposited."[4]).

Nevertheless, after Darwin the role of any intelligent agent such as God was pushed so much into the background that for all practical purposes He ceased to exist for the world of biology and for science in general. It was soon taken for granted that if life could have evolved into complex forms on its own, then life itself could have started without any intelligent agent.

Darwin's proposal caught on wildly, and in its wake it ushered in a modern era of materialism, or naturalism – the idea that material nature and the universe are closed, self-contained units and that to explain anything within them, including our selves, our feelings, our thoughts, and our consciousness, we need refer to nothing beyond the laws that govern matter, the laws of physics and chemistry.

But in spite of the widespread acceptance of Darwinism and its attendant materialism, Darwin's theory has always had its scientific critics, and their number has not decreased. Rather, and to the surprise of many, the criticism has greatly increased. Since the late 1980s, evolution has faced opposition from a growing number of members of the scientific community itself. This opposition has gradually united into an Intelligent Design front and pulled the world of science into what has been called "the Evolution War."

What Intelligent Design (ID) entails will be explained in the chapters to follow. But for now let me give a simple definition: Intelligent Design is the theory that infers signs of intelligence from the workings of nature. What this means becomes clearer if for a moment we turn to the field of archeology. Archeologists study discovered objects, such as flints, and ask the question whether everything about these objects can be explained naturally or whether, on the contrary, certain traits are the result of intentional work by humans. When archeologists determine that a discovered object could not have been shaped by natural processes alone, they infer design and regard the object as a human artifact. Similarly, ID is the attempt by scientists to draw a line between what could have been caused by nature working alone and what could not have and must therefore have been caused by an intelligent agent.

What makes ID controversial is not that it tries to discriminate between designed and naturally formed objects per se, since this goes on not only in archeology but in many fields of science, but that contemporary design-theorists look for and claim to have found signs of intelligence in nature and life. Living organisms, they say, have features that cannot be ascribed to the laws of nature alone but are best explained as artifacts of an intelligent cause. Of course, this at once puts ID in opposition to Darwinism and evolutionary theory, which precisely claim that everything about life can be explained materially.

This explains why the face-off between evolutionists and proponents of Intelligent Design creates such a stir. Critics accuse ID of being veiled religion, whereas design theorists retort that ID is no more a religion than Darwinism – or perhaps only just as much. ID scientists say that since they demonstrate their conclusions entirely from studies of nature and not by recourse to religious concepts or scripture, ID cannot be called "religion" in any usual sense of the term. But if Intelligent Design should be called religious because it has religious implications – which everyone agrees it has – then Darwinism is also religious. The only difference between the two is that Intelligent Design points to an intelligent cause behind nature whereas Darwinism purports to show that an intelligent cause for life and nature is not necessary. Perhaps the real fact is that, whether one likes it or not, the discussion about the nature of life invariably overlaps both science and religion.

What science has to say about the nature of life has implications for more than just an elite group of experts. The question of life's origin and development influences every human being's self-understanding and indeed lies at the foundation of how we each build ideas of what is true and false, right and wrong, important and unimportant, and about the meaning of existence. This may be one more reason why this issue causes so much stir.

In this book, assisted by Jonathan Wells, Michael Behe, William Dembski, and Michael Cremo, I first offer the reader an understanding of what Darwinism and Intelligent Design are. Next, while agreeing with the basic ideas of Intelligent Design, I go one step further by examining evidence normally not a direct part of the Intelligent Design discussion – in particular, studies of consciousness, parapsychological phenomena, inspiration, and evidence pointing to a conscious self that can exist apart from matter. Some may consider this a risky step, but upon examination one finds much high-quality scientific evidence in this field that opens a window on a nonphysical yet still observable reality. This, of course, can have great implications for how we understand the nature of life.

Finally, in the book's last chapter, I try to weave all these disparate strands of evidence together into a whole. Evidence never stands alone in science; it must be interpreted into a broader theoretical framework, often called a paradigm. For most modern biologists, the guiding paradigm is Darwin's theory of evolution. In the words of evolutionary biologist Theodosius Dobzhansky (1900–1975), "Nothing in biology makes sense except in the light of evolution" and "There are no alternatives to evolution as history that can withstand critical examination."[5] In this book's last chapter, I take up Dobzhansky's challenge and propose such an alternative.

As I have said, I have drawn my paradigm from the *Vedas*,[6] the ancient Sanskrit writings of Hindu India. From the viewpoint of modern science, the Vedic literature, apart from its philosophical content, records some astonishingly accurate details about the universe. Astrophysicist Carl Sagan (1934–1996) noted in his book *Cosmos:*

> The Hindu religion is the only one of the world's great faiths dedicated to the idea that the Cosmos itself undergoes an immense, indeed an infinite, number of deaths and rebirths. It is the only religion in which the time scales correspond to those of modern scientific cosmology. Its cycles run from our ordinary day and night to a day and night of Brahma, 8.64 billion years long. Longer than the age of the Earth or the Sun and about half the time since the Big Bang.[7]

Of course, that the ages of the earth and the universe given in the Vedic literature roughly coincide with the figures discovered by modern science is something Sagan considered accidental. But is it? My own feeling is that at least we should consider whether there may be more to the Vedic literature than meets the eye.

While there are numerous schools of Vedic thought, I have chosen to draw inspiration from one: the Gaudiya Vaishnava teachings given by the prominent Vedic scholar A. C. Bhaktivedanta Swami Prabhupada (1896–1977), founder and preceptor of the International Society for Krishna Consciousness. Prabhupada wrote more than fifty books on Vedic culture. Educated at a British college in Calcutta during the British Raj, he was also familiar with Western science and philosophy. In his work discussing thirty-five prominent Western philosophers, he accepted Darwin to have been the most influential on modern thought. His critique of Darwinism, given in a series of conversations with Dr. Thoudam Singh, a chemist and student of Nobel laureate Harold Urey,[8] was published in 1976 in a much circulated book titled *Life Comes From Life*.

To form a meeting place for Vedic philosophy and modern science, Prabhupada established a research center known as the Bhaktivedanta Institute, with its main branch in Mumbai, India. In the years since his death, researchers associated with the Bhaktivedanta Institute have published numerous books and papers on modern science and Vedic thought, many of which have dealt specifically with Darwin's theories. This book is a footnote to their effort.

In conclusion, I owe gratitude to many for contributing to this book. First, I again have to express my deep and heartfelt thanks to Jonathan Wells, Michael Behe, and William Dembski. Although both they and I know they do not agree with everything in my Vedic presentation, they broadmindedly agreed to contribute to this book. I thank Michael Cremo, who not only wrote the chapter "Human Origins and the Archeological Record" but also served as a close advisor while I was writing and gave many valuable suggestions. Several scientists have reviewed and critiqued the manuscript in full or in part during its writing. In particular, biologist Dr. Jerry Bergman of Northwest State College, Ohio, USA, reviewed the entire manuscript midways. Among others who similarly helped were Denyse O'Leary, Phillip Johnson, Walter ReMine, Günther Momsen, Arne Kiilerich, and Krishna Kripa Dasa. My thanks are to all of them. The responsibility for whatever shortcomings remain in the book despite their careful scrutiny and advice is my own.

Many others have also made significant contributions. I thank Kaisori Bellach for her untiring work of editing, and Brahma Muhurta Dasa for being a visionary publisher willing to undertake this publication. Jayadvaita Swami and Ksama Dasi deserve special mention for their editing and proofreading. Krishna Kripa also worked on the notes and the bibliography. I thank Ramaprasada Dasa for his work on the illustrations, and Govinda Dasa for the design and layout. Finally, my deep gratitude to my wife, Dandaniti Devi Dasi, for her encouragement and patience during the writing of this book.

Leif Asmark Jensen (Lalitanatha Dasa)

CHAPTER 1

The Origin of Species

E ven though Darwin's ideas were considered revolutionary in Victorian England, natural evolution was no novel concept when in 1859 he published *On the Origin of Species*. Some philosophers and scientists of the eighteenth and nineteenth centuries had already been toying with the idea that species were not stable – that is, that they could change and, over time, become new species. Scientists like the French naturalist Jean-Baptiste Lamarck (1744–1829) and Charles Darwin's grandfather, Erasmus Darwin (1731–1802), had been exploring the idea for years. However, no one had been able to convincingly suggest a natural mechanism that could be driving evolution, and so natural evolution had remained a fringe idea.

Apparently, Darwin was not an adherent of evolution (or what it implies) in his younger years. Rather, at least according to official biographies, he was a strong believer in the Bible, trained in Christian theology. As he later described, "I did not then in the least doubt the strict and literal truth of every word in the Bible."[1] And according to the Bible, creation had taken place just a few thousands – and not millions – of years earlier, when over a period of six days God had created each species – each type of plant, animal, and human being – separately.

Darwin is supposed to have changed his outlook, however, while undertaking a five-year voyage (1831–1836) to some of the remotest corners of earth as a naturalist aboard the HMS *Beagle*. His travels took him to the bottom of South America and to the windswept shores of the Galapagos Islands in the Pacific Ocean, 970 kilometers off the coast of Ecuador. There he encountered much that didn't fit his understanding of Biblical creation. He saw geological wonders – volcanoes and rock strata – that pointed to an earth much older than the six thousand years the Bible allowed. Of course, he had already encountered the idea that the earth was more ancient than he had previously supposed when he read British geologist Charles Lyell's *Principles of Geology*, the first volume of which was published just a year before Darwin set out. In *Principles* Lyell proposed that the earth's geological structure was a result not of a recent creation but of slow natural forces operating almost invisibly over millions and millions of years. Darwin felt what he saw on his voyage confirmed Lyell's hypothesis.

Aside from geological questions, Darwin also found himself puzzled

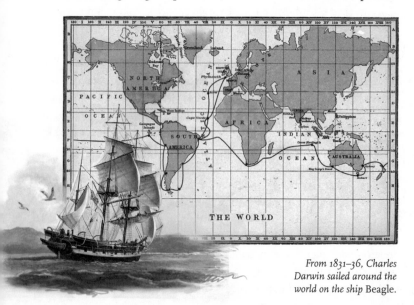

From 1831–36, Charles Darwin sailed around the world on the ship Beagle.

by the geographical distribution of species. That the Galapagos alone hosted many distinct yet obviously related species of plants and animals scattered over a few small islands sowed in his mind the seeds of the idea of organic evolution. He wrote in his journal, "It is the circumstance, that several of the islands possess their own species of the tortoise, mocking-thrush, finches, and numerous plants, these species having the same general habits, occupying analogous situations, and obviously filling the same place in the natural economy of this archipelago, that strikes me with wonder."[2]

If species had been created separately, then why had God created different yet very similar species for each of the small islands, the smallest of which were, in Darwin's words, barely more than "points of rock"? It would have made more sense if completely different species inhabited each island. This phenomenon, something Darwin began to notice everywhere he traveled, led him to think that perhaps the species had not been created separately at all but had evolved from a common ancestor in the distant past.

When Darwin returned to England in 1836 he continued to ponder the issue and gradually became convinced of organic evolution. In 1844 he wrote a friend, "At last gleams of light have come, and I am almost convinced (quite contrary to the opinion I started with) that species are not (it is like confessing a murder) immutable."[3]

As other naturalists of Darwin's time also observed the geographical distribution of species, they too became convinced of evolution. One such naturalist was Alfred Russel Wallace (1823–1913), a young correspondent of Darwin's who now and then sent Darwin plant and animal specimens from his travels in Borneo. Wallace shares with Darwin the honor of having proposed the theory of evolution, because while Darwin had written down his thoughts privately, he had never published his theory. Wallace had found the time to spell out his ideas on evolution through natural selection while he was bedridden with malaria in Borneo. He detailed his thoughts in a paper he sent to Darwin, asking him to send on both the letter and the paper to Charles Lyell, whom Wallace did not know. It is said that Darwin was dismayed to receive Wallace's paper[4] – Darwin had been quietly working on the same ideas for twenty years by this time. Now the younger Wallace was about to receive credit for the theory Darwin considered his own. Of course, there were differences between Darwin's conception and Wallace's conception. Darwin had focused on the uniqueness of species and Wallace on the driving force of natural selection. But both had drawn their ideas from Malthus's paper on population economics. When Darwin mentioned Wallace's letter to Charles Lyell, Lyell encouraged him to copublish the theory with Wallace. Wallace readily agreed to share the spotlight, and on July 1, 1858, their joint paper was presented to the Linnean Society of London. This was the official birth of the theory of evolution through natural selection.

The theory drew little notice at first – it was only one of several papers read at the Linnean Society that summer – but it came more into the light a year later when, on November 22, Darwin published *On the Origin of Species*. The book was an overnight bestseller and somewhat eclipsed Wallace's role in the theory's development. From then on, the theory of evolution has been almost exclusively attributed to Charles Darwin.

What made Darwin's and Wallace's theory unique was that it proposed what appeared to be a plausible natural mechanism to account for how the numerous species scattered over the earth had come about: they had evolved from a common ancestor by the processes of variation and natural selection. As mentioned previously, others had long ago presented ideas about evolution, but no one had yet presented a plausible driving mechanism. Lamarck, for example, had proposed that evolution was fueled by a nebulous vital force or inner urge common to all living organisms. Darwin and Wallace, however, confined their theory to "variation" and "natural selection" as sufficient mechanisms to create variety in life.

Darwin's theory can be summarized in a few words: Every species contains variations among individuals in terms of size, ability, color, pattern, etc., and some of these differences prove advantageous for an organism in its competition for survival with other members of the same species. Individuals with advantageous traits live longer and produce more offspring than those without them. When these more adept individuals reproduce, they pass on their advantageous traits to their offspring; concomittantly, the less adept fail to pass on their less advantageous traits because they often fail to survive long enough to reproduce, or they manage to produce significantly fewer offspring than more favored individuals. Gradually, the species comes to contain *only* individuals with the advantageous traits; those traits that disadvantage the species become extinct. This process of "natural selection" causes a species to develop in particular directions and can eventually lead to the development of a new species.

To support the idea of natural selection, Darwin relied heavily, in his research, on the artificial breeding of plants and animals. We only have to look around the agricultural world to see how breeding for specific traits can appear to change one species almost entirely. Breeding dogs has resulted in both Great Danes and poodles, with every conceivable variety in between. Darwin was himself an expert breeder of pigeons and argued that if man can cause sweeping changes in a species through artificial selection after only a few generations, then nature must have been able to accomplish incredible feats after eons. He felt it was conceivable that anything could happen through natural selection, including that humans and all other species could gradually develop from previously existing species, which themselves had evolved from other species, which had developed in their ancient histories from the simplest of microbes.

The Downfall of Darwinism

Darwin's theory is undoubtedly simple and elegant. But is it true? This, of course, was the central question during Darwin's lifetime, and it remains the central question to this day. Considering the enormous impact Darwin's theory has had over the last 150 years, many people may be surprised to learn that within decades of its being proposed scientists had come to see that it was obviously *not* true. Today, virtually no serious scientist believes in Darwin's theory as he proposed it.

Rather, they have come to believe in some form of neo-Darwinism, a later development that agrees with Darwin on only two points: that evolution from a common ancestor took place and that it occurred through natural processes alone.

To make the difference between Darwinism and neo-Darwinism clear, it is useful to look at what was wrong with Darwin's original theory. This will also allow us to see how some people, including certain biologists, unwittingly cling to some of the ideas that have otherwise been rejected for well over a century.

Varieties and Species

The standard definition of a species for sexually-reproducing organisms requires that members of the same species can mate and create fertile offspring. If two organisms engage in sex and cannot produce offspring capable of further propagation of their own species, the two organisms belong to different species. Darwin agreed with this definition.[5]

Taxonomy teaches us that species are divided into varieties, also known as races or sorts. However, varieties, unlike species, do not have strong demarcations between them; that is, they can crossbreed freely and produce fertile offspring. Their offspring will still belong to their species even if the crossbreeding produces a new variety. The various races of humans are an example of the effect of crossbreeding. All humans, regardless of race (variety), can propagate and produce fertile offspring.

The crux of Darwin's argument is that *varieties can gradually become species through breeding*. In other words, he believed that the changes that appear in the varieties within a species can be extended unlimitedly:

> Nevertheless, according to my view, varieties are species in the process of formation, or are, as I have called them, incipient species. How, then, does the lesser difference between varieties become augmented into the greater difference between species? That this does habitually happen we must infer from most of the innumerable species throughout nature presenting well-

marked differences; whereas varieties, the supposed prototypes and parents of future well-marked species, present slight and ill-defined differences.[6]

In short, Darwin believed that plant and animal breeding can give rise to new species. The first chapter in *Origin,* "Variation Under Domestication," examines the effect human-directed breeding has on a species. Although he doesn't state it outright, Darwin implies that if given enough time and enough crossbreeding, species could be bred until they become a new species. In his second chapter, "Variation Under Nature," Darwin argues that nature also has the capability to breed varieties until they become new species through the process of natural selection.

As it turned out, Darwin was wrong about how much change actually occurs in varieties. Therefore he was also wrong to think that new species could arise given enough crossbreeding. We now know that nature has placed limits on how far a species can change. Breeding can affect differences only in preexisting characteristics. For example, by breeding dogs one can produce dogs of different sizes, temperaments, or hair length and color. But whether short or tall, the dogs remain dogs. It is not possible to breed for character-

Even though of all kinds of sizes, from Great Danes to tiny poodles, varieties of dogs always remain dogs and never become new species through breeding.

istics that are not already present in dogs. We will never be able to produce a cat by breeding dogs, even if we breed through many generations. Breeding simply shuffles and recombines already existing traits.

We have also discovered that there are limits even on how much one can enhance or suppress the inherent characteristics. The American botanist and plant breeder Luther Burbank (1849–1926) stated:

I know from experience that I can develop a plum half an inch long or one two-and-a-half inches long, with every possible length in between, but I am willing to admit that it is hopeless to try to get a plum the size of a small pea, or one as big as a grapefruit. I have roses that bloom pretty steadily for six months of the year, but I have none that will bloom twelve, and I will not have. In short, there are limits to the development possible.[7]

The noted French zoologist Pierre Grassé (1895–1985) agreed:

In spite of the intense pressure generated by artificial selection (eliminating any parent not answering the criteria of choice) over whole millennia, no new species are born. A comparative study of sera, hemoglobins, blood proteins, interfertility, etc., proves that the strains remain within the same specific definition. This is not a matter of opinion or subjective classification, but a measurable reality. The fact is that selection gives tangible form to and gathers together all the varieties a genome is capable of producing, but does not constitute an innovative evolutionary process.[8]

In 1982, Francis Hitching wrote similarly about selective breeding:

It is now absolutely clear that there are firm natural limits to what can be done. Remarkable achievements can be made by crossbreeding and selection inside the species barrier, or within a larger circle of closely related species, such as wheats. But wheat is still wheat, and not, for instance, grapefruit. Between 1800 and 1878, the sugar content of beets was raised from 6 to 17 per cent. A half century of further breeding failed to make any difference."[9]

All this was not only demonstrated in the years following Darwin; before and during his time biologists had already correctly observed that there were limits to the changes one could effect through breeding. Darwin's notion that varieties could turn into species was wishful thinking and not based on actual evidence.

Pangenesis – The Inheritance of Acquired Traits

The other thing Darwin got wrong was the mechanism of inheritance, and this soon became obvious as the science of genetics advanced. While he conceded his ignorance ("The laws governing inheritance are quite unknown"[10]), he still made assumptions about how they worked. It was later shown that they didn't work in the way he had thought.

Natural selection alone is not enough to create a new species. Natural selection cannot create; it can only eliminate. The Dutch scientist Hugo de Vries pointed out that natural selection may explain the *survival* of the fittest but not the *arrival* of the fittest.[11] Even more important than natural selection is the appearance of favorable variations. As Darwin himself noted, "...unless profitable variations do occur, natural selection can do nothing."[12] For example, there could be no breeding of new dog races if all dogs were born completely identical. Natural selection has to have some variation to select from in order for evolution to take place.

Darwin believed that the variation needed for his theory was provided by external influences on the organisms. He believed that food and environment affect and change the organisms, as do how organisms use – or not use – their organs. These effected changes would then be passed on through the generations. Darwin wrote,

> The great and inherited development of the udders in cows and goats in countries where they are habitually milked, in comparison with the state of these organs in other countries, is another instance of the effect of use [that causes changes in the organisms].[13]

And,

> From the facts alluded to in the first chapter, I think there can be little doubt that use in our domestic animals strengthens and

enlarges certain parts, and disuse diminishes them; and that such modifications are inherited.[14]

Darwin also thought that experience (external influences) and the traits acquired through experience affected the "reproductive elements," the semen and egg cells. This is why these traits were passed on in new variations. He writes, "But I am strongly inclined to suspect that the most frequent cause of variability may be attributed to the male and female reproductive elements having been affected prior to the act of conception."[15]

Darwin was wrong in assuming that either environment or natural selection creates new characteristics.

Darwin shared this idea with Lamarck, who had suggested that giraffes who stretch their necks to eat the leaves other giraffes cannot reach develop longer necks and in turn produce calves with longer necks. However, all these ideas are now known to be incorrect. Acquired traits are not inherited. We may lift weights until we develop muscles like steel, but our children will not be born with larger muscles. In some cultures where women enhance their beauty by enlarging their lips or earlobes, their daughters are not born with bigger lips or earlobes than girls in any other culture. It is not true that cows develop larger udders when milked and pass this trait to their calves, or that a species exposed to the cold develops fur, fat layers, and a higher metabolism and adds these traits into its genetic makeup to be passed on to its offspring. Darwin was wrong in assuming that either environment or natural selection creates new characteristics. Natural selection simply eliminates those individuals that don't have the favorable traits already.

Just when Darwin was publishing *Origin* Gregor Mendel (1822–1884), an Austrian monk living in the Augustinian monastery of Brno, was studying the laws of inheritance. Mendel is an exemplar of both a deeply religious man and a staunch scientist. In his research he performed extensive experiments crossing different varieties of plants and noting how their characteristics were passed from one generation to the next. Especially well known are his experiments with peas.

Mendel's research demonstrated anything but the evolution that Darwin envisioned. Mendel observed no genetic changes in species over the generations. In 1866, only seven years after Darwin had published his book, Mendel published his treatise *Versuche über Pflanzen-hybriden* (*Experiments on Plant Hybridization*), in which he introduced "the laws of constant elements." The word "constant" appeared in his paper sixty-seven times – "constant characters," "constant offspring," "constant combinations," "constant forms," "constant law," "a constant species," etc. Mendel concludes that heredity involves a transmission of constant factors that determine an organism's traits. Although the factors can be mixed and matched during reproduction, they remain discrete and unchanging from one generation to the next.[16]

The laws of inheritance Mendel discovered were opposite to the laws Darwin had assumed. A simple way to understand the difference between the two views is to think of a deck of cards. By shuffling the deck, one can combine the cards in quite a large number of ways, but no new cards will arise in the process. This was Mendel's correct view of inheritance. Darwin, on the other hand, incorrectly imagined that new cards, i.e., previously nonexisting traits, could arise by shuffling the cards around. Jonathan Wells explains it like this:

> [Darwin] believed that every cell in an organism produces "gen-mules" that transmit characteristics to the next generation in a blending process he called "pangenesis." The advantage of Darwin's view was that genmules could be changed by external influences, or by use and disuse, and thus account for evolutionary change. The disadvantage of Darwin's view was that it was false.[17]

Although Mendel's paper was published in 1866, it was ignored for decades, perhaps because of its anti-evolutionary implications and Mendel's own opposition to evolution. It wasn't until several years after his death that his work was appreciated and his laws of inheritance became the cornerstone of modern genetics.

Of course, all this is old news. Mendelian genetics has been firmly established for more than a century. Amazingly, however, one can still meet evolutionary scientists who appeal to Darwin's concept of the inheritance of acquired traits. American biologist Christopher Wills writes,

> The force that seems to have accelerated our brain's growth is a new kind of *stimulant:* language, signs, collective memories – all elements of culture. As our cultures evolved in complexities, so did our brains, which then drove our cultures to still greater complexity. Big and clever brains led to more complex cultures, which in turn led to bigger and cleverer brains.[18] [emphasis added]

Here a biology professor, as late as 1993, is appealing to an external factor, a "stimulant," to explain how a new trait (bigger brains) arose. It is surprising to see the concept of pangenesis still showing up in modern evolutionary thought. One would expect today's biologists to have a better explanation than pangenesis for a complex organ like the human brain.[19]

Darwinism as Dogma

The cornerstones of Darwin's theory are that varieties can evolve into new species and that acquired traits are inherited. The work of Mendel and others refutes both of these. One might ask, Then what happened to the idea of natural evolution? Did scientists revisit the idea that species may have been created separately – or that they may have been created at all? Did they consider the possibility that more than natural mechanisms were operating in nature?

The answer is no to both questions. But to understand why, we need to study the impact Darwinism had not just on science but on society as a whole. From the last decades of the nineteenth century on, Darwinism became as much a worldview as a scientific hypothesis. In his 2007 book *Darwin Day in America,* Dr. John G. West discusses how by the beginning of the twentieth century Darwin's theory had pervaded all of Western society and culture and replaced the more traditional ways of understanding life. This in turn led to many of the socio-political events of the first half of the twentieth century. John West:

> At the dawn of the last century, leading scientists and politicians giddily predicted that modern science – especially Darwinian biology – would supply solutions to all the intractable problems of American society, from crime to poverty to sexual maladjustment. Instead, politics and culture were dehumanized as a new generation of "scientific" experts began treating human beings as little more than animals or machines:
>
> - In criminal justice, these experts denied the existence of free will and proposed replacing punishment with invasive "cures" such as the lobotomy.
> - In the welfare department they proposed eliminating the poor by sterilizing those deemed biologically unfit.
> - In business, they urged the selection of workers based on racist theories of human evolution and the development of advertising methods to more effectively manipulate consumer behavior.
> - In sex education, they advocated creating a new sexual morality based on "normal mammalian behavior," without regard to long-standing ethical or religious imperatives.[20]

Darwinism thus permeated society with far-reaching consequences, and as it did, the theory left the realm of hypothesis and moved into the realm of "established fact," something not to be doubted. It was no longer a question of *whether* evolution had taken place but of how.

A comment made by Wallace is revealing. Wallace later differed with Darwin on a number of points (discussed in chapter 12), including Darwin's idea that evolution was an unguided, natural process. Rather, he came to see evolution as part of God's great plan to place eternal souls in physical bodies for spiritual evolution.[21] In a 1903 interview, the eighty-year-old Wallace was asked if he thought scientists would become more spiritually minded. His reply reveals his opinion of what Darwinism had done to scientific minds:

> I do [think scientists will become more spiritual], but the process is a very slow one. The attitude of science was probably never more materialistic than now... Spiritual scientific men are very few, and most of them are afraid of revealing their mind. The majority of scientists seem to regard it as a sign of insanity to avow belief in any other than what are called the ordinary laws of nature.[22]

In his 1991 book, *Darwin on Trial,* Berkeley law professor Phillip Johnson explores how the central Darwinian concept of descent with modification from a common ancestor became dogma rather than science and over time stopped being tested as hypotheses are usually tested:

> We can only speculate about the motives that led scientists to accept the concept of common ancestry so uncritically. The triumph of Darwinism clearly contributed to a rise in the prestige of professional scientists, and the idea of automatic progress so fit the spirit of the age that the theory even attracted a surprising amount of support from religious leaders. In any case, scientists did accept the theory before it was rigorously tested, and thereafter used all their authority to convince the public that naturalistic processes are sufficient to produce a human from a bacterium, and a bacterium from a mix of chemicals. Evolutionary science became the search for confirming evidence, and the explaining away of negative evidence.[23]

Johnson illustrates his opinion with an interesting incident. In 1967, the Wistar Institute in Philadelphia, USA, hosted a conference called

"Mathematical Challenges to the Neo-Darwinian Interpretation of Evolution." At the conference leading mathematicians met with leading evolutionary biologists and argued the statistical impossibility that complex organs, such as the eye, could have evolved by a series of thousands upon thousands of small, random mutations; the number of mutations needed to create a complex eye is simply far too large, and there just hasn't been time in the world's history for these random mutations to have occurred. Instead of acknowledging the problem, however, the biologists accused the mathematicians of "doing science backwards." Evolution, they said, was an established fact; the eye *had* evolved. So the mathematical problems could not be reflecting reality. A leading attendee at the conference, evolutionist Ernst Mayr, said, "Somehow or other by adjusting these figures we will come out all right. We are comforted by the fact that evolution has occurred."[24]

Evolutionists have become so convinced that evolution is a fact and not a theory that at times they have even been unable to clearly distinguish between fact and theory. A prominent spokesperson for evolution in the latter part of the twentieth century, Harvard paleontologist Stephen Jay Gould (1941–2002), once wrote:

Facts are the world's data. Theories are structures of ideas that explain and interpret facts. Facts do not go away while scientists debate rival theories for explaining them. Einstein's theory of gravity replaced Newton's, but apples did not suspend themselves in midair pending the outcome. And human beings evolved from apelike ancestors whether they did so by Darwin's proposed mechanism or by some other, yet to be identified.[25]

Phillip Johnson notes,

The analogy is spurious. We observe directly that apples fall when dropped, but we do not observe a common ancestor for modern apes and humans. What we *do* observe is that apes and humans are physically and biochemically more like each other than they are like rabbits, snakes, or trees. The apelike common ancestor is a hypothesis in a *theory*, which purports to explain how these greater and lesser similarities came about. The theory is plausible, especially to a philosophical materialist, but it may nonetheless be false. The true explanation for natural relationships may be something much more mysterious.[26]

One can even find examples of evolutionists who are so convinced of evolution that they accidentally cite evidence that actually counters it. Tim Berra is an example of one such evolutionist. In his 1990 book, *Evolution and the Myth of Creationism,* Berra tried to help readers understand why the fossil record establishes descent from a common ancestor. He compared fossils to a series of automobile models: "If you compare a 1953 and a 1954 Corvette, side by side, then a 1954 and a 1955 model, and so on, the descent with modification is overwhelmingly obvious. This is what [paleontologists] do with fossils, *and the evidence is so solid and comprehensive that it cannot be denied by reasonable people.*"[27] [emphasis in the original]

> **Evolution became dogma in Darwin's time and has remained dogma ever since.**

Phillip Johnson dubbed this "Berra's blunder" because everyone knows that cars are designed in advance by intelligent designers and that each car is manufactured separately. Their similarity is not the result of an unguided Darwinian process of descent dependent on reproduction. What Berra actually showed is that resemblances between species can be due to design; similarities found in the fossil record might as easily be due to common design as common descent. But because he was so convinced about the "fact" of evolution, he saw even a contradictory example as evidence for evolution.

In short, evolution became dogma in Darwin's time and has remained dogma ever since. Although much could be argued against his proposed mechanisms of evolution, most evolutionary scientists today refuse to look at the evidence and instead have taken on the task of finding mechanisms to account for what they already accept as fact.

Neo-Darwinism: The Modern Synthesis

Darwinism was dealt a serious blow when it was shown that acquired characteristics could not be inherited. The inheritance of acquired characteristics was then replaced with the idea that mutations must have caused genetic variation. Scientists could see that although inherited characteristics remain stable and unchanging from one generation to the next, on rare occasions there are genetic changes. These changes, originally called "freaks of nature" and later "mutations," became the proposed source of the new genetic material needed for evolution to occur. And with the discovery in the 1950s of the DNA double helix, scientists learned that mutations are caused by random errors taking place when the genetic code, which is stored in the DNA, is copied.

What is now known as Neo-Darwinism, or "the Modern Synthesis," was the result of an attempt by leading biologists between 1936 and 1947 to formulate a theory of biological origins that reconciled Mendelian genetics with Darwin's concept of evolution from a common ancestor. The biologists concluded that organisms evolve due to small changes caused by random mutations "sifted" through natural selection.

Here it must be recognized that the mechanism proposed by the Neo-Darwinians is much weaker than the mechanism originally proposed by Charles Darwin. Darwin's mechanism of acquired traits is almost deterministic in nature. If food is scarce for long enough and the only way to survive is to stretch your neck and consume what no other member of your species can reach, then over the generations, your descendants will certainly develop a longer neck and become long-necked giraffes. But to achieve the same result through random mutation is a different story. The number of random mutations required to evolve a long neck do not happen simply because long necks are advantageous at any given moment. Since the mutations are random, they may or may not occur, and most likely they will *not* occur at the moment when they have the best chance of being useful.

Random mutations, we now know, account for very few novel and favorable traits, even though this mutation idea has been widely accepted for almost a century. That mutations occur is not at issue. What is in doubt is how they advantage an organism, since most mutations have been shown to be either neutral (having no effect) or detrimental. The medical libraries are full of books listing mutations and the harmful conditions and diseases they cause, but the literature rarely reveals examples of mutations benefiting organisms.

In fact, almost the only examples given of beneficial mutations are those that make bacteria resistant to antibiotics. Other examples address how the mutation that causes sickle-cell anemia – a mutation that kills 25 percent of its human hosts – also provides resistance to malaria. Thus in spite of a 25 percent mortality rate from sickle-cell disease, those possessing this mutation in malaria-infected areas have a greater chance of surviving malaria than those who do not.

In his 2007 book *The Edge of Evolution* Michael Behe asks how much mutations can actually achieve. He tries to answer this question by exploring a number of cases, some in which evolution did occur and some in which it did not. Take malaria, for example. Malaria has killed an amazing number of humans in recorded history, yet although the malaria parasite has been around for tens of thousands of years, it can live only in the tropics. Malarial parasites cannot reproduce in temperatures below 16 degrees Celsius. An obvious question: Why hasn't this parasite evolved the ability to tolerate lower temperatures and thus enabled itself to spread to colder climates? Certainly it has had plenty of opportunity to do so because, as Behe points out, with its staggering reproductive capacity and short generation time there have been more malarial parasites on earth in the last ten thousand years than mammals in the last two hundred million years.

But as it turns out, if the malarial parasite is to adapt to lower temperatures, multiple coherent genetic mutations would be needed – more mutations than one can expect to take place randomly and concurrently. Behe concludes, through this and other examples, that if more than one mutation is needed for an organism to evolve, Darwinian evolution begins to become improbable; the more mutations needed, the more exponential the decrease in probability that Darwinian processes will be able to achieve a particular system.

Thus although neo-Darwinism has been in vogue for more than a century, no satisfactory mechanism exists to account for how evolution occurs. This was further seen when, in 2008, the Konrad Lorenz Institute in Austria invited the world's leading theoretical biologists to a conference called "Toward an Extended Evolutionary Synthesis." The organizers explained themselves in their invitation:

> The challenge seems clear to us: how do we make sense, conceptually, of the astounding advances in biology since the 1940s, when the [Modern Synthesis] was taking shape? Not only have we witnessed the molecular revolution, from the discovery of the structure of DNA to the genomic era, we are also grappling with the increasing feeling that we just don't have the theoretical and analytical tools necessary to make sense of the bewildering diversity and complexity of living organisms.[28]

Could it be clearer? Evolutionists today seem to have an "increasing feeling" that they don't have the "theoretical tools" to explain "the bewildering diversity and complexity of living organisms."

The Search for Speciation

Not only is there no satisfactory mechanism to account for how new species appear, but speciation (the forming of new species) has never been observed. As was true in Darwin's day, variations within a species are readily observed, but "evolution" beyond variations is still hypothetical. Still, one can find some who contest this assessment. Whole lists have been posted on the internet of instances of speciation, often drawn from prominent scientists' statements.[29] But without exception all these examples deal with variations within particular species and not with speciation.[30]

Darwin's finches are one commonly cited example of supposed

speciation. The Galapagos Islands are located almost a thousand kilometers off the coast of Ecuador. There one finds a number of finch species called Darwin's finches. When Darwin first visited these islands he paid little attention to these birds. Later, however, it was seen that although they vary in size and color, the finches all appear to have originated from a single strain, birds that probably migrated from somewhere on the American continent, and thus provide an excellent example of Darwinian evolution.

Yet although the finches appear to have a common ancestor, they are not a true instance of speciation because when they mate they produce fertile offspring. Some of the species actually appear to be remerging. In other words, the finches offer an example not of speciation but of variation within a species.[31]

Another oft cited example is the herring gull. The herring gull and the lesser black-backed gull form what is known as a "ring species." These birds appear in Europe as two separate species, but if one were to follow the herring gull east through Russia and Siberia into North America, Greenland, Iceland, and back to Europe, one would see that the herring gull gradually becomes more and more like the lesser black-backed gull. The evidence is strong that they have branched out from one ancestral gull species, and especially in Europe that they have become two species that do not interbreed.

Yet it turns out that they are *able* to breed and produce fertile off-

spring. What keeps them from doing so is not biological inability but a difference in behavior. Again, this is not an example of true speciation but another variation within a species.[32]

To sum up, bacteriologist Alan H. Linton writes,

The herring gull and the lesser black-backed gull form what is known as a "ring species."

[Nothing] exists in the literature claiming that one species has been shown to evolve into another. Bacteria, the simplest form of independent life, are ideal for this kind of study, with generation times of twenty to thirty minutes, and populations achieved after eighteen hours. But throughout 150 years of the science of bacteriology, there is no evidence that one species of bacteria has changed into another... Since there is no evidence for species changes between the simplest forms of unicellular life, it is not surprising that there is no evidence for evolution from prokaryotic to eukaryotic cells, let alone throughout the whole array of higher multicellular organisms.[33]

In 2002, evolutionary biologists Lynn Margulis and Dorion Sagan echoed Linton:

Speciation, whether in the remote Galapagos, in the laboratory cages of the drosophilosophers, or in the crowded sediments of the paleontologists, still has never been traced.[34]

The theory of evolution, whether in Darwin's original formulation or in the formulation of neo-Darwinism, still lacks an evidential confirmation. The origin of species is as much a mystery today as it was when Darwin published his book 150 years ago.

If we have never witnessed the formation of new species, what do evolutionists have to offer in support of their theory? In the chapter that follows, biologist Jonathan Wells takes a close look at some of the most often cited evidences of evolution.

CHAPTER 2

Survival of the Fakest

Jonathan Wells

Science now knows that many of the pillars of Darwinian theory are either false or misleading. Yet biology texts continue to present them as factual evidence of evolution. What does this imply about their scientific standards?

I f you had asked me during my years studying science at Berkeley whether or not I believed what I read in my science textbooks, I would have responded much as any of my fellow students: puzzled that such a question would be asked in the first place. One might find tiny errors, of course, typos and misprints. And science is always discovering new things. But I believed – took it as a given – that my science textbooks represented the best scientific knowledge available at that time.

It was only when I was finishing my Ph.D. in cell and development biology, however, that I noticed what at first I took to be a strange anomaly. The textbook I was using prominently featured drawings of vertebrate embryos – fish, chickens, humans, etc. – where similarities were presented as evidence for descent from a common ancestor. Indeed, the drawings did appear very similar. But I'd been studying embryos for some time, looking at them under a microscope. And I knew that the drawings were just plain wrong.

I rechecked all my other textbooks. They all had similar drawings, and they were all obviously wrong. Not only did they distort the embryos they pictured; they omitted earlier stages in which the embryos look very different from one another.

Like most other science students, like most scientists themselves, I let it pass. It didn't immediately affect my work, and I assumed that while the texts had somehow gotten this particular issue wrong, it was the exception to the rule. In 1997, however, my interest in the embryo drawings was revived when British embryologist Michael Richardson and his colleagues published the result of their study comparing the textbook drawings with actual embryos. As Richardson himself was quoted in the prestigious journal *Science:* "It looks like it's turning out to be one of the most famous fakes in biology."

Worse, this was no recent fraud. Nor was its discovery recent. The embryo drawings that appear in most every high school and college textbook are either reproductions of, or based on, a famous series of drawings by the 19th century German biologist and fervent Darwinian Ernst Haeckel, and they have been known to scholars of Darwin and evolutionary theory to be forgeries for over a hundred years. But none of them, apparently, have seen fit to correct this almost ubiquitous misinformation. Still thinking this an exceptional circumstance, I became curious to see if I could find other mistakes in the standard biology texts dealing with evolution. My search revealed a startling fact, however: Far from being exceptions, such blatant misrepresentations are more often the rule. In my recent book I call them "Icons of Evolution" because so many of them are represented by classic oft-repeated illustrations which, like the Haeckel drawings, have served their pedagogical purpose only too well – fixing basic misinformation about evolutionary theory in the public's mind.

We all remember them from biology class: the experiment that created the "building blocks of life" in a tube; the evolutionary "tree," rooted in the primordial slime and branching out into animal and plant life. Then there were the similar bone structures of, say, a bird's wing and a man's hand, the peppered moths, and Darwin's finches. And, of course, the Haeckel embryos.

As it happens, all of these examples, as well as many others purportedly standing as evidence of evolution, turn out to be incorrect. Not just slightly off. Not just slightly mistaken. On the subject of Darwinian evolution the texts contained massive distortions and even some faked evidence. Nor are we only talking about high school textbooks that some might excuse (but shouldn't) for adhering to a lower standard. Also guilty are some of the most prestigious and widely used college texts, such as Douglas Futuyma's *Evolutionary Biology*, and the latest edition of the graduate-level textbook *Molecular Biology of the Cell*, coauthored by the president of the National Academy of Sciences, Bruce Alberts. In fact, when the false "evidence" is taken away, the case for Darwinian evolution, in the textbooks at least, is so thin it's almost invisible.

Life in a Bottle

Anyone old enough in 1953 to understand the import of the news remembers how shocking, and to many, exhilarating, it was. Scientists Stanley Miller and Harold Urey had succeeded in creating "the building blocks" of life in a flask. Mimicking what were believed to be the natural conditions of the early earth's atmosphere, and then sending an electric spark through it, Miller and Urey had formed simple amino acids. As amino acids are the "building blocks" of life, it was thought just a matter of time before scientists could themselves create living organisms. At the time, it appeared a dramatic confirmation of evolutionary theory. Life wasn't a "miracle." No outside agency or divine intelligence was necessary. Put the right gasses together, add electricity, and life is bound to happen. It's a common event. Carl Sagan could thus confidently predict on PBS that the planets orbiting those "billions and billions" of stars out there must be just teeming with life.

There were problems, however. Scientists were never able to get beyond the simplest amino acids in their simulated primordial environment, and the creation of proteins began to seem not a small step or couple of steps, but a great, perhaps impassable, divide. The telling blow to the Miller-Urey experiment, however, came in the 1970s, when scientists began to conclude that the earth's early atmosphere was nothing like the mixture of gasses used by Miller and Urey. Instead of being what scientists call a "reducing," or hydrogen-rich environment, the earth's early atmosphere probably consisted of gasses released by volcanoes. Today there is a near consensus among geochemists on this point. But put those volcanic gasses in the Miller-Urey apparatus, and the experiment doesn't work – in other words, no "building blocks" of life.

What do textbooks do with this inconvenient fact? By and large they ignore it and continue to use the Miller-Urey experiment to convince students that scientists have demonstrated an important first step in the origin of life. This includes the above-mentioned *Molecular Biology of the Cell*, coauthored by the National Academy of Sciences president, Bruce Alberts. Most textbooks also go on to tell students that origin-of-life researchers have found a wealth of other evidence to explain how life originated spontaneously – but they don't tell students that the researchers themselves now acknowledge that the explanation still eludes them.

Faked Embryos

Darwin thought "by far the strongest single class of facts in favor of" his theory came from embryology. Darwin was not an embryologist, however, so he relied on the work of German biologist Ernst Haeckel, who produced drawings of embryos from various classes of vertebrates to show that they are virtually identical in their earliest stages, and become noticeably different only as they develop. It was this pattern that Darwin found so convincing.

This may be the most egregious of distortions, since biologists have known for over a century that vertebrate embryos never look as similar as Haeckel drew them. In some cases, Haeckel used the same woodcut

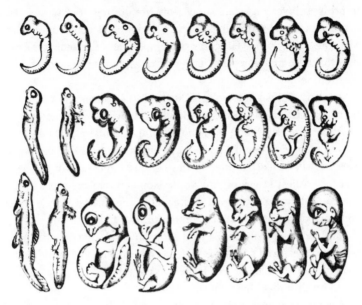

Haeckel's faked embryo drawings. The embryos are (from left to right) fish, salamander, tortoise, chick, hog, calf, rabbit, and human. This faked illustration showing purported similarities between these embryos is from Darwinism Illustrated *by* George Romanes *from 1892.*

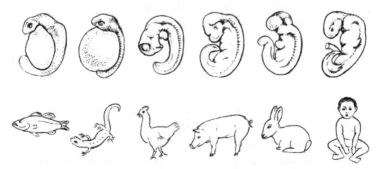

The embryo stages as they really are. The embryos are (from left to right) fish, salamander, chicken, pig, rabbit, and human. Please notice that the stage Haeckel labeled "first" is actually a later stage in embryonic development. At the true first stage, all the embryos differ radically from one another.

to print embryos that were supposedly from different classes. In others, he doctored his drawings to make the embryos appear more alike than they really were. Haeckel's contemporaries repeatedly criticized him for these misrepresentations, and charges of fraud abounded in his lifetime.

In 1997, British embryologist Michael Richardson and an international team of experts compared Haeckel's drawings with photographs of actual vertebrate embryos, demonstrating conclusively that the drawings misrepresent the truth. The drawings are misleading in another way. Darwin based his inference of common ancestry on the belief that the earliest stages of embryo development are the most similar. Haeckel's drawings, however, entirely omit the earliest stages, which are much different, and start at a more similar midway point.

Embryologist William Ballard wrote in 1976 that it is "only by semantic tricks and subjective selection of evidence," by "bending the facts of nature," that one can argue that the early stages of vertebrates "are more alike than their adults."

Yet some version of Haeckel's drawings can be found in most current biology textbooks. Stephen Jay Gould, one of evolutionary theory's most vocal proponents, recently wrote that we should be "astonished and ashamed by the century of mindless recycling that has led to the persistence of these drawings in a large number, if not a majority, of modern textbooks." (I will return below to the question of why it is only now that Mr. Gould, who has known of these forgeries for decades, has decided to bring them to widespread attention.)

Darwin's Tree of Life

Darwin wrote in *The Origin of Species:* "I view all beings not as special creations, but as the lineal descendants of some few beings" that lived in the distant past. He believed that the differences among modern species arose primarily through natural selection, or survival of the fittest, and he described the whole process as "descent with modification."

No one doubts, of course, that a certain amount of descent with modification occurs within species. But Darwin's theory claims to

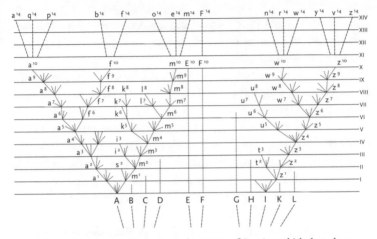

Darwin's tree of life, the only illustration in his Origin of Species, *which shows how he saw the species having evolved from the most simple of species, at the bottom, and gradually become more variegated and diverged.*

account for the origin of new species – in fact, for every species since the first cells emerged from the primordial ooze.

This theory does have the virtue of making a prediction: If all living things are gradually modified descendants of one or a few original forms, then the history of life should resemble a branching tree. Unfortunately, despite official pronouncements, this prediction has in some important respects turned out to be wrong.

The fossil record shows the major groups of animals appearing fully formed at about the same time in a "Cambrian explosion," rather than diverging from a common ancestor. Darwin knew this, and considered it a serious objection to his theory. But he attributed it to the imperfection of the fossil record, and he thought that future research would supply the missing ancestors.

But a century and a half of continued fossil collecting has only aggravated the problem. Instead of slight differences appearing first, then greater differences emerging later, the greatest differences appear right at the start. Some fossil experts describe this as "top-down evolution," and note that it contradicts the "bottom-up" pattern predicted by Darwin's theory. Yet most current biology textbooks don't even mention the Cambrian explosion, much less point out the challenge it poses for Darwinian evolution.

Then came the evidence from molecular biology. Biologists in the 1970s began testing Darwin's branching tree pattern by comparing molecules in various species. The more similar the molecules in two different species are, the more closely related they are presumed to be. At first this approach seemed to confirm Darwin's tree of life. But as scientists compared more and more molecules, they found that different molecules yield conflicting results. The branching-tree pattern inferred from one molecule often contradicts the pattern obtained from another.

Canadian molecular biologist W. Ford Doolittle doesn't think the problem will go away. Maybe scientists "have failed to find the 'true tree'," he wrote in 1999, "not because their methods are inadequate or because they have chosen the wrong genes, but because the history of life cannot properly be represented as a tree."

Nevertheless, biology textbooks continue to assure students that Darwin's Tree of Life is a scientific fact overwhelmingly confirmed by evidence. Judging from the real fossil and molecular evidence, however, it is an unsubstantiated hypothesis masquerading as a fact.

They All Look Alike: Homology in Vertebrate Limbs

Most introductory biology textbooks carry drawings of vertebrate limbs showing similarities in their bone structures. Biologists before Darwin had noticed this sort of similarity and called it "homology," and they attributed it to construction on a common archetype or design. In *The Origin of Species*, however, Darwin argued that the best explanation for homology is descent with modification, and he considered it evidence for his theory.

Darwin's followers rely on homologies to arrange fossils in branching trees that supposedly show ancestor-descendant relationships. In his 1990 book *Evolution and the Myth of Creationism*, biologist Tim

Berra compared the fossil record to a series of Corvette models: "If you compare a 1953 and a 1954 Corvette, side by side, then a 1954 and a 1955 model, and so on, the descent with modification is overwhelmingly obvious."

But Berra forgot to consider a crucial, and obvious, point: Corvettes, so far as anyone has yet been able to determine, don't give birth to little Corvettes. They, like all automobiles, are designed by people working for auto companies. In other words, an outside intelligence. So although Berra believed he was supporting Darwinian evolution rather than the pre-Darwinian explanation, he unwittingly showed that the fossil evidence is compatible with either. Law professor (and critic of Darwinism) Phillip E. Johnson dubbed this "Berra's Blunder."

"The tree of cars." Different old and new models of cars and vehicles can also be arranged in a hierarchical structure. One would be wrong, however, to conclude that this tree of car evolution implies that cars developed through an unguided Darwinian process. This example shows that similarity may be due to design (cars are designed) as well as to natural evolution.

The lesson of Berra's Blunder is that we need to specify a natural mechanism before we can scientifically exclude designed construction as the cause of homology. Darwinian biologists have proposed two mechanisms: developmental pathways and genetic programs. According to the first, homologous features arise from similar cells and processes in the embryo; according to the second, homologous features are programmed by similar genes.

But biologists have known for a hundred years that homologous structures are often not produced by similar developmental pathways. And they have known for thirty years that they are often not produced by similar genes, either. So there is no empirically demonstrated mechanism to establish that homologies are due to common ancestry rather than common design.

Without a mechanism, modern Darwinists have simply defined homology to mean similarity due to common ancestry. According to Ernst Mayr, one of the principal architects of modern neo-Darwinism: "After 1859 there has been only one definition of homologous that makes biological sense: Attributes of two organisms are homologous when they are derived from an equivalent characteristic of the common ancestor."

This is a classic case of circular reasoning. Darwin saw evolution as a theory and homology as its evidence. Darwin's followers assume evolution is independently established, and homology is its result. But you can't then use homology as evidence for evolution except by reasoning in a circle: Similarity due to common ancestry demonstrates common ancestry.

Philosophers of biology have been criticizing this approach for decades. As Ronald Brady wrote in 1985: "By making our explanation into the definition of the condition to be explained, we express not scientific hypothesis but belief. We are so convinced that our explanation is true that we no longer see any need to distinguish it from the situation we were trying to explain. Dogmatic endeavors of this kind must eventually leave the realm of science."

So how do the textbooks treat this controversy? Once again, they ignore it. In fact, they give students the impression that it makes sense to define homology in terms of common ancestry and then turn around and use it as evidence for common ancestry. And they call this "science."

Nothing a Little Glue Can't Fix: The Peppered Moths

Darwin was convinced that in the course of evolution, "Natural Selection has been the most important, but not the exclusive, means of modification," but he had no direct evidence of this. The best he could do in *The Origin of Species* was give "one or two imaginary illustrations."

In the 1950s, however, British physician Bernard Kettlewell provided what seemed to be conclusive evidence of natural selection. During the previous century, peppered moths in England had gone from being predominantly light-colored to being predominantly dark-colored. It was thought that the change occurred because dark moths are better camouflaged on pollution-darkened tree trunks and thus less likely to be eaten by predatory birds.

To test this hypothesis experimentally, Kettlewell released light and dark moths onto nearby tree trunks in polluted and unpolluted woodlands, then watched as birds ate the more conspicuous moths. As expected, birds ate more light moths in the polluted woodland, and more dark moths in the unpolluted one. In an article written for *Scientific American,* Kettlewell called this "Darwin's missing evidence." Peppered moths soon became the classic example of natural selection in action, and the story is still retold in most introductory biology textbooks, accompanied by photographs of the moths on tree trunks.

In the 1980s, however, researchers discovered evidence that the official story was flawed – including the pertinent fact that peppered moths don't normally rest on tree trunks. Instead, they fly by night and apparently hide under upper branches during the day. By releasing moths onto nearby tree trunks in daylight, Kettlewell had created an artificial situation that does not exist in nature. Many biologists now consider his results invalid, and some even question whether natural selection was responsible for the observed changes.

So where did all those textbook photos of peppered moths on tree trunks come from? They were all staged. To expedite things, some photographers even glued dead moths to trees. Of course, the people who staged them before the 1980s thought they were accurately representing the true situation, but we now know they were mistaken. Yet a glance at almost any current biology textbook reveals that they are all still being used as evidence for natural selection.

In 1999, a Canadian textbook writer justified the practice: "You have to look at the audience. How convoluted do you want to make it for a first-time learner?" Bob Ritter was quoted as saying in the April 1999 *Alberta Report Newsmagazine.* High school students "are still very concrete in the way they learn," continued Ritter. "We want to get across the idea of selective adaptation. Later on, they can look at the work critically."

Apparently, the "later" can be *much* later. When University of Chicago professor Jerry Coyne learned the truth in 1998, he was well into his career as an evolutionary biologist. His experience illustrates how insidious the icons of evolution really are, since they mislead experts as well as novices.

Beaks and Birds: Darwin's Finches

A quarter of a century before Darwin published *The Origin of Species,* he was formulating his ideas as a naturalist aboard the British survey ship HMS *Beagle.* When the *Beagle* visited the Galapagos Islands in 1835, Darwin collected specimens of the local wildlife, including some finches. Though the finches had little in fact to do with Darwin's development of evolutionary theory, they have attracted considerable attention from modern evolutionary biologists as further evidence of natural selection. In the 1970s, Peter and Rosemary Grant and their colleagues noted a 5 percent increase in beak size after a severe drought, because the finches were left with only hard-to-crack seeds. The change, though significant, was small; yet some Darwinists claim it explains how finch species originated in the first place.

A 1999 booklet published by the U.S. National Academy of Sciences describes Darwin's finches as "a particularly compelling example" of the origin of species. The booklet cites the Grants' work, and explains how "a single year of drought on the islands can drive evolutionary changes in the finches." The booklet also calculates that "if droughts occur about once every 10 years on the islands, a new species of finch might arise in only about 200 years."

But the booklet fails to point out that the finches' beaks returned to normal after the rains returned. No net evolution occurred. In fact, several finch species now appear to be merging through hybridization rather than diverging through natural selection as Darwin's theory requires.

Withholding evidence in order to give the impression that Darwin's finches confirm evolutionary theory borders on scientific misconduct. According to Harvard biologist Louis Guenin (writing in *Nature* in 1999), U.S. securities laws provide "our richest source of experiential guidance" in defining what constitutes scientific misconduct.

But a stock promoter who tells his clients that a particular stock can be expected to double in value in twenty years because it went up 5 percent in 1998, while concealing the fact that the same stock declined 5 percent in 1999, might well be charged with fraud. As Berkeley law professor Phillip E. Johnson wrote in *The Wall Street Journal* in 1999: "When our leading scientists have to resort to the sort of distortion that would land a stock promoter in jail, you know they are in trouble."

From Apes to Humans

Darwin's theory really comes into its own when it is applied to human origins. While he scarcely mentioned the topic in *The Origin of Species*, Darwin later wrote extensively about it in *The Descent of Man*. "My object," he explained, "is to show that there is no fundamental difference between man and the higher animals in their mental faculties" – even morality and religion. According to Darwin, a dog's tendency to imagine hidden agency in things moved by the wind "would easily pass into the belief in the existence of one or more gods."

Of course, the awareness that the human body is part of nature was around long before Darwin. But Darwin was claiming much more. Like materialistic philosophers since ancient Greece, Darwin believed that human beings are nothing more than animals. Darwin, however, needed evidence to confirm his conjecture. Although Neanderthals had already been found, they were not then considered ancestral to humans, so Darwin had no fossil evidence for his view.

It wasn't until 1912 that amateur paleontologist Charles Dawson announced that he had found what Darwinists were looking for, in a gravel pit at Piltdown, England. Dawson had found part of a human skull and part of an apelike lower jaw with two teeth. It wasn't until forty years later that a team of scientists proved that the Piltdown skull, though perhaps thousands of years old, belonged to a modern human, while the jaw fragment was more recent, and belonged to a modern orangutan. The jaw had been chemically treated to make it look like a fossil, and its teeth had been deliberately filed down to make them look human. Piltdown Man was a forgery.

Most modern biology textbooks do not even mention Piltdown. When critics of Darwinism bring it up, they are usually told that the incident merely proves that science is self-correcting. And so it was, in this case – though the correction took over forty years. But the more interesting lesson to be learned from Piltdown is that scientists, like everyone else, can be fooled into seeing what they want to see.

The same subjectivity that prepared the way for Piltdown continues to plague human-origins research. According to paleoanthropologist Misia Landau, theories of human origins "far exceed what can be inferred from the study of fossils alone and in fact place a heavy burden of interpretation on the fossil record – a burden which is relieved by placing fossils into pre-existing narrative structures."

> **Biology students and the general public are rarely informed of the deep-seated uncertainty about human origins.**

In 1996, American Museum of Natural History Curator Ian Tattersall acknowledged that "in paleoanthropology, the patterns we perceive are as likely to result from our unconscious mindsets as from the evidence itself." Arizona State University anthropologist Geoffrey Clark echoed this view in 1997 when he wrote: "We select among alternative sets of research conclusions in accordance with our biases and preconceptions." Clark suggested that "paleoanthropology has the form but not the substance of science."

Biology students and the general public are rarely informed of the deep-seated uncertainty about human origins that is reflected in these statements by scientific experts. Instead, they are simply fed the latest speculation as though it were a fact. And the speculation is typically illustrated with fanciful drawings of cavemen, or pictures of human actors wearing heavy make-up.

What's Going on Here?

Most of us assume that what we hear from scientists is comparatively trustworthy. Politicians might distort or shave the truth to support a preconceived agenda, but scientists, we are told, deal with facts. Sure they might sometimes get it wrong, but the beauty of science is that it's empirically testable. If a theory is wrong, this will be discovered by other scientists performing independent experiments either to replicate or disprove their results. In this way the data are constantly reviewed and hypotheses become widely accepted theories. So how do we explain such a pervasive and long-standing distortion of the specific facts used to support evolutionary theory?

Perhaps Darwinian evolution has taken on a significance in our culture that has little to do with its scientific value, whatever that may be. An indication of this was seen in the nearly universal and censorious reaction to the Kansas School Board's decision to allow room for dissent in the standard teaching of evolution (much of which, as we have just seen, is plain wrong). According to the news media, only religious fundamentalists question Darwinian evolution. People who criticize Darwinism, we are told, want to bomb science back to the Stone Age and replace it with the Bible.

The growing body of scientific evidence contradicting Darwinian claims is steadfastly ignored. When biochemist Michael Behe pointed out in *The New York Times* last year that the embryo "evidence" for evolution was faked, Harvard Darwinist Stephen Jay Gould admitted that he had known this for decades (as noted above) – but accused Behe of being a "creationist" for pointing it out. Now, although Behe supports the idea that some features of living things are best explained by intelligent design, he is not a "creationist" as that word is normally used. Behe is a molecular biologist whose scientific work has convinced him that Darwinian theory doesn't conform to observation and experimental evidence. Why does Gould, who knows Haeckel's drawings were faked, dismiss Behe as a creationist for criticizing them? I suspect that there's an agenda other than pure science at work here. My evidence is the more or less explicit materialist message woven into many textbook accounts. Futuyma's *Evolutionary Biology* is characteristic of this, informing students that "it was Darwin's theory of evolution," together with Marx's theory of history and Freud's theory of human nature, "that provided a crucial plank to the platform of mechanism and materialism" that has since been "the stage of most Western thought." One textbook quotes Gould, who openly declares that humans are not created but are merely fortuitous twigs on a "contingent" (i.e., accidental) tree of life. Oxford Darwinist Richard Dawkins, though not writing in a textbook, puts it even more bluntly: "Darwin made it possible to be an intellectually fulfilled atheist."

These are obviously philosophical rather than scientific views. Futuyma, Gould, and Dawkins have a right to their philosophy. But they do not have the right to teach it as though it were science. In science, all theories – including Darwinian evolution – must be tested against the evidence. Since Gould knows that the real embryological evidence contradicts the faked drawings in biology textbooks, why doesn't he take a more active role in cleaning up science education? The misrepresentations and omissions I've examined here are just a small sampling. There are many more. For too long the debate about evolution has assumed "facts" that aren't true. It's time to clear away the lies that obstruct popular discussion of evolution, and insist that theories conform to the evidence. In other words, it's time to do science as it's supposed to be done.

CHAPTER 3

The Fossil Record

The dictionary defines a fossil as "a remnant or trace of an organism of a past geologic age, such as a skeleton or leaf imprint, embedded and preserved in the earth's crust." Any plant or animal can be preserved, often becoming petrified, if buried quickly enough and under the right conditions; yet only a small fraction of organisms become fossils. Most decompose or are eaten by scavengers. Still, during the vast number of years it has taken the earth to reach its current age, billions of organisms have been fossilized. These fossils have created a veritable history book, a "record of the rocks," of life on earth.

It is widely believed that fossils provide strong evidence for Darwin's theory of evolution. A publication put out in 2008 by the U.S. National Academy of Sciences (NAS) called *Science, Evolution, and Creationism* claims that "fossil discoveries have continued to produce new and compelling evidence about evolutionary history" and that "the fossil record provides extensive evidence documenting the occurrence of evolution."[1]

What NAS doesn't tell us is that ever since Darwin's time, the fossil record has posed – and continues to pose – a challenge to the theory of evolution. Rather than documenting smooth, gradual transitions from one species to another or from one or a few simple species to a plethora of complex species, the fossil record consistently shows a pattern in which species appear suddenly and fully formed, then exist virtually unchanged until they disappear altogether from the fossil layers. Charles Darwin was aware of this pattern and addressed it in *The Origin of Species:*

> [T]he number of intermediate varieties, which have formerly existed, [must] be truly enormous. Why then is not every geological formation and every stratum full of such intermediate links? Geology assuredly does not reveal any such finely-graduated organic chain; and this, perhaps, is the most obvious and serious objection which can be urged against the theory.[2]

During Darwin's time the geological layers outside Europe and North America were still largely unexplored. Today, paleontologists have carried out excavations worldwide and from all periods of the earth's history. They have uncovered hundreds of thousands of extinct species. But not a single intermediate species or chain of species has been found. By 1954, Professor Nils Heribert-Nilsson from Lund University in Sweden concluded,

> The fossil material is now so complete that … the lack of transitional series cannot be explained as due to the scarcity of the material. The deficiencies are real; they will never be filled.[3]

In 1979 the paleontologist David Raup concurred:

> [W]e are now about 120 years after Darwin, and knowledge of the fossil record has been greatly expanded … ironically, we have even fewer examples of evolutionary transition than we had in Darwin's time.[4]

And paleontologist Niles Eldredge wrote in 1995:

> No wonder paleontologists shied away from evolution for so long. It never seemed to happen. Assiduous collecting up cliff faces yields zigzags, minor oscillations, and the very occasional slight accumulation of change – over millions of years, at a rate too slow to account for all the prodigious change that has occurred in evolutionary history. When we do see the introduction of evolutionary novelty, it usually shows up with a bang, and often with no firm evidence that the fossils did not evolve elsewhere! Evolution cannot forever be going on somewhere else. Yet that's how the fossil record has struck many a forlorn paleontologist looking to learn something about evolution.[5]

In 2008 Niles Eldredge affirmed his 1995 statement:

> [P]atterns in evolutionary history characteristically repeat themselves regardless of position in time, place, or clade. The pattern [is one of] rapid-seeming appearance of higher taxa with their defining adaptations/synapomorphies already well in place in the earliest known fossils – implying a very rapid evolutionary origin, often leaving no trace of intermediates.[6]

American paleontologist Stephen Jay Gould expressed this opinion:

> The history of most fossil species includes two features particularly inconsistent with gradualism:
>
> - Stasis. Most species exhibit no directional change during their tenure on earth. They appear in the fossil record looking pretty much the same as when they disappear; morphological change is usually limited and directionless.
> - Sudden appearance. In any local area, a species does not

arise gradually by the steady transformation of its ancestors;
it appears all at once and "fully formed."[7]

The Imperfection of the Geological Record

Darwin himself ascribed the lack of intermediate forms to "the extreme
imperfection of the geological record."[8] He argued that since only a
fraction of what dies is fossilized, the geological record would necessarily be incomplete.

However, although most living organisms never become fossils,
Bill Dembski and Jonathan Wells both argue that there is still good
reason to consider the fossil record a fairly complete picture of the history of life on earth.[9] *How* complete that picture is can be understood
by assessing how well current life forms are represented in the fossil
record; this will give us an idea of the degree to which species in general tend to be preserved as fossils.

As it turns out, the majority of modern life forms appear in the fossil record. Dembski and Wells note: "For instance, among 43 known living orders of terrestrial vertebrates (the level of classification just below
classes and phyla), 42 have been found as fossils. Thus, 98 percent
of extant terrestrial vertebrates at that level of classification were fossilized.... Among 329 known living families of terrestrial vertebrates
(the level of classification just below orders), 261 have been found as
fossils – that's a fossilization percentage of almost 80 percent. If one
removes birds (which tend to be poorly fossilized), then among 178
living families..., 156 have been found as fossils – that's a fossilization percentage of almost 88 percent. A fossilization percentage of 66
percent at the level of genera is not uncommon."[10]

In light of these findings it does seem that most organisms are represented in the fossil record. If this is true, then Darwin was wrong to
think that the lack of intermediate forms can be ascribed to incomplete
fossilization in the geological record.

This gives a different perspective on another of Darwin's predic-
tions. In *Origin* he writes, "... by this theory innumerable transitional
forms must have existed."[11] Evolutionists often refer to the hundreds

of millions, even billions, of species that must have existed. However, the actual catalogued number of both plants and animals is not in the billions but is about 200,000 to 300,000 extinct fossil species. This can be contrasted to the approximately 1.8 million still-living species, including those that have become extinct during recorded history. In other words, the millions of intermediate species Darwin predicted have never been found, and there is little reason to believe they ever will. The fossil record indicates that such species never existed.

Punctuated Equilibrium

To preserve Darwin's evolutionary theory paleontologists have come up with a variety of explanations for the lack of transitional forms. In the 1940s the German-American geneticist Richard Goldschmidt proposed the "hopeful monster" theory, the idea that one species suddenly gave birth to a radically different species – a dinosaur giving birth to a bird, perhaps. Although his idea was ridiculed, that he threw it into the ring reflects the very real concern over the troubling lack of transitional forms in the fossil record.

In the 1970s Stephen Jay Gould and Niles Eldredge introduced the idea of punctuated equilibrium. While not rejecting Darwin's idea of gradual evolution as Richard Goldschmidt had, they proposed that evolution had run a somewhat different course than most evolutionists had hitherto assumed. Instead of a gradual shaping and changing of large populations of species into new species over long periods of time, they proposed that evolutionary changes and speciation had taken place rapidly and only in small isolated populations that had been subject to environmental pressure. When the isolation was broken after a geological instant (a few tens or hundreds of thousands of years), a new species would suddenly appear and out-compete the old species from which it had branched. This explains why the fossil record shows stasis followed by sudden bursts of change. One may then ask where the fossils of those isolated populations are that gave rise to new species. According to this theory, the species existed far too briefly and in areas so small and isolated that the species could not have left many fossils.

The theory of punctuated equilibrium does seem to explain the lack of transitional forms without changing the basic mechanism of Darwinian evolution, but there is no way to test it. Its main prediction, in the end, is that the fossil record will continue to lack evidence. There could, of course, be other reasons for this lack of evidence. Perhaps the species were created and did not evolve at all, for example. In any case, there is no way to prove and thereby establish the theory to the exclusion of other possibilities.

The Cambrian Explosion

From the standpoint of the evidence now accepted by modern paleontologists, one of the most puzzling features of the fossil record as it is currently understood is what is called the "Cambrian explosion." During the Cambrian period an abundance of complex multicellular life appeared suddenly – within as brief a period as five to ten million years, a blink of the eye, geologically speaking. These forms seemed to appear out of nowhere. Where did they come from?

Although the debate still goes on, according to most paleontologists life on earth can be traced back to about 3.6 to 3.8 billion years ago. That is, life forms seem to have inhabited the earth almost immediately after it is supposed to have cooled off enough to sustain life as we know it. Certain fossil evidence of single-celled organisms goes back about two billion years.[12] This means that for more than three billion years – about 80 percent of life's history – there are only traces of unicellular organisms, such as bacteria. According to the evidence currently accepted by mainstream paleontologists, the first multicellular organisms are about 700 million years old. These organisms were first discovered in the Ediacara Hills of Australia. Oddly enough, these organisms do not appear to be related to or ancestral to modern organisms. According to the evidence currently accepted by mainstream paleontologists, modern forms of life arose during the Cambrian explosion. That is, *suddenly* there was an abundance of multicellular, complex life – organisms as complex as they are today.

To understand the significance of this, one needs to be aware of the classification system biologists use to categorize species. The system was invented by the Swedish naturalist Carolus Linnaeus, who classified animals and plants according to species, genus (plural, genera), family, order, class, phylum (plural, phyla), and kingdom. By this system humans belong to the species *sapiens,* the genus *Homo,* the family *Hominidae,* the order of primates, the class of mammals, the phylum of chordates, or vertebrates, and the kingdom of animals.

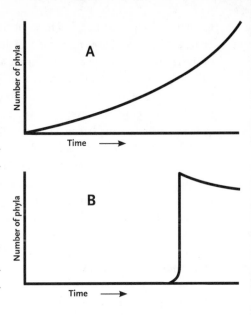

The Cambrian Explosion turns Darwin's tree upside down. Graph A shows how Darwin predicted the evolution of the variety of life, with life becoming more variegated with time. Graph B shows what really happened. For three billion years only unicellular organisms existed, then at the beginning of the Cambrian multicellular life suddenly appeared, apparently out of nowhere, exhibiting more variety at this point in the history of earth than at any later point in time.

According to Darwin's theory, life evolved from one or a few species, whose varieties, at first, closely resembled one another but which gradually diverged and became new species. Over time these still-similar species diverged further and became different genera. These in turn, after long periods of time, evolved into different families, which gradually became different orders, classes, phyla, and kingdoms. Darwin illustrated this prediction with the only graphic in *Origin* (see Darwin's tree, page 37).

But the Cambrian explosion turns Darwin's tree – and this part of his theory – upside down. Suddenly the earth was teeming with as many as sixty new phyla, the second highest level of classification. The fossil record shows no traces of these phyla before the Cambrian period. Some evolutionists have suggested that the reason there were no traces of these phyla is that before the Cambrian living organisms had only soft body parts. That is, they didn't fossilize well. But there are countless examples of fossilized soft tissue. Some prominent examples were found in the fauna discovered in the Ediacara Hills. The Cambrian explosion was real and has to be accounted for.

What makes the Cambrian explosion all the more striking is that the phyla we see today appeared for the most part during the Cambrian period. There are a few exceptions that seem to have appeared in the following period, the Ordovician, but many paleontologists suspect that they too arose in the Cambrian even if the fossil record doesn't show it yet. No more phyla have appeared over the past 500 million years. One has no choice but to question Darwin's prediction of a very gradual, almost invisible evolution from simple to more complex organisms.

Example of Transitions?

Scientists admit that the fossil record rarely shows intermediate species. Still, they nevertheless allege that there are several examples of transition documented by the fossils. Let's look at a couple of these.

After the theory of punctuated equilibrium was published, many anti-evolutionists used Gould's and Eldredge's statements about the lack of transitional forms to criticize the theory of evolution. Gould felt obliged to defend Darwinism, and without withdrawing his previous acknowledgment of the lack of transitional forms, he modified his position. Now he claimed that there were at least two good examples of transitional forms in the fossil record. First, he cited the evolution of humans, a process supported by an uninterrupted sequence of fossils dating from the present to about three or four million years ago. Why these dates, along with the whole scenario of human evolution, are open for debate is the topic of Michael Cremo's article "Human Origins and the Archeological Record" (see chapter 9). Gould's other example referred to the transition from reptiles to mammals. Douglas Futuyma's standard college textbook on evolution explains it like this:

The origin of mammals, via mammal-like reptiles, from the earliest amniotes is doubtless the most fully, beautifully documented example of the evolution of a major taxon. In no other case are as many steps preserved in the fossil record. The origin of mammals definitely refutes creationists' claims that fossils fail to document evolution. It also shows how characteristics can become highly modified to serve new functions.[13]

But although Futuyma goes on to detail a sequence stretching over 150 million years, Dembski and Wells point out that things are not as clear-cut as he claims.[14] This becomes especially apparent when we read how Futuyma, in a different context, gives this qualifying statement:

The gradual transition from therapsid reptiles to mammals is so abundantly documented by scores of species in every stage of transition that it is impossible to tell which therapsid species were the actual ancestors of modern mammals.[15]

According to Futuyma it is not possible to tell exactly which species were the ancestors of modern mammals. Then how do we know any of them were? If paleontologists had found, in one place or within one geological area, an unbroken sequence of reptiles gradually evolving into mammals, the case for reptile-mammal evolution would be strong. But no such sequence has ever been found. As it turns out, the collection of mammal-like reptiles and reptilelike mammals has been gathered from around the world and from all periods within a span of 150 million years. It has been proven that some of the ancestors actually appeared in the fossil record *after* their supposed descendants. Evolutionists have an answer to this conundrum: the ancestral species need not have left fossils until after their descendants did. By this they mean that they existed before their descendants, but we simply haven't yet found their early fossils – or perhaps they didn't leave early fossils. This is a possibility, of course, but unless and until these fossils are found, this idea has not been scientifically proven.

It is important to note that species can share similarities without being related in an evolutionary sense. For example, the giant panda and the red panda are similar animals, and both have the "panda's thumb," a particular wrist bone that helps the panda grasp bamboo shoots. It would seem natural to consider the two species homologous, but they are not. According to present evolutionary understanding the two kinds of pandas evolved from a common ancestor that lacked this modified wrist, and the development of the "thumb" in both is considered an instance of convergent evolution (see chapter 5 on convergence).

If it is not possible to discern an evolutionary relationship when two animals share such a distinctive trait, how can anyone conclude in cases where similarities are more remote that two species share an evolutionary relationship – as scientists have tried to do in conveniently arranging the fossils of reptiles and mammals? There are no grounds on which one can draw such a conclusion.

Do Feathered Dinosaurs Really Exist?

Since the middle of the 1990s another example of intermediates in the fossil record has received much attention: the transition from dinosaurs to birds. Many now consider this one of the strongest refutations of the claim that there are no instances of transitional forms. These days, most evolutionary biologists will be able to cite a number of instances of alleged fossilized dinosaurs preserved with either feathers or "proto feathers," a downlike substance considered to have been developed by the reptilian ancestors of birds to insulate themselves against the cold. Many scientists consider this transition so well established as to be beyond discussion. The paleontologist Richard Prum wrote in 2003: "It is time to end debate on the therapod origin of birds, and to proceed to investigate all aspects of the biology of birds in their therapod origin."[16]

Prum's comment was directed toward a small number of fellow scientists who still refused to accept the otherwise almost universal view that birds evolved from the class of reptiles broadly known as therapods. Comments like Prum's have resulted in a hot debate behind the scenes in the paleontological world. The skeptics are not anti-evolutionists; they simply haven't found the evidence for feathered dinosaurs convincing.

One of these skeptics is paleornithologist Alan Feduccia from the University of North Carolina, USA. He stated in 1997:

> Well, I've studied bird skulls for twenty-five years and I don't see any similarities whatsoever. I just don't see it... The theropod origin of birds, in my opinion, will be the greatest embarrassment of paleontology of the twentieth century.[17]

In "Do Feathered Dinosaurs Exist?", a paper published in 2005 partly in response to Richard Prum, Feduccia and two colleagues presented the results of a study they had completed of all the alleged dinosaur fossils with feathers. They concluded that the supposed proto feathers were not actually feathers but decomposed collagen, a protein that makes up a major portion of skin. Feduccia et al. also conducted a study on decomposing skin from sharks and dolphins. They found that the collagen in these animals developed similar structures as those associated with proto feathers. Furthermore, they pointed to examples of the same structure found in other extinct reptiles not considered related to birds. Feduccia and his colleagues wrote,

> [I]t is probably too early to declare that "it is time to abandon debate on the theropod origin of birds" (Prum, 2002). Abandoning debate may succeed in concealing problems rather than finding solutions to important scientific questions. The problem of avian origins is far from being resolved.[18]

Larry Martin, a paleontologist from the University of Kansas, USA, is another skeptic. He supports Feduccia's conclusions but adds that some of the examples of dinosaurs with real feathers are actually "secondarily flightless Mesozoic birds." By this he means that "feathered dinosaurs" are not actually reptiles but early birds that, like ostriches, had lost or had never possessed the ability to fly. He writes:

Examples of feathered dinosaurs result from erroneous identification of internal structures as part of the skin covering, and from the confusion of flightless birds from the Early Cretaceous of China with dinosaurs.[19]

In a 2008 study published in *The Proceedings of the Royal Society, Biological Sciences*,[20] Theagarten Lingham-Soliar, a paleontologist in the Zoology department of the University of Durban-Westville, attacks the interpretation of proto feathers in the Chinese fossils. A comment by him appeared in the British newpaper *The Daily Telegraph* in January 2008: "Scientists must really now choose – belief in the nebulous idea of proto feathers or the reality of collagen, the dominant protein in vertebrates ... I am convinced from the nonsense spouted by many of the people who denounce collagen in favor of proto feathers that they have never actually seen collagen in its natural or decomposing state."[21]

Tiktaalik

A third example given of an intermediate form in the fossil record is *Tiktaalik*, a fossil found in 2004 and presented as an intermediate between fish and tetrapods. Tetrapod, "four-footed," refers to amphibians, reptiles, birds, and mammals.

In April 2006 the media enthusiastically reported the discovery at Ellesmere Island in northern Canada of *Tiktaalik roseae*, a fish touted as a fishapod. *Nature* wrote, "[T]his is 'the fish that crawled out of water' – a true 'missing link.'"[22] *Scientific American* followed suit: "Newfound Fossil is Transitional between Fish and Landlubbers."[23] Almost overnight, *Tiktaalik* attained iconic status, "confirming elements of a major transition in evolution."[24]

However, although *Tiktaalik* has retained its iconic status in the public's mind, with closer scrutiny *Tiktaalik* has some of the same problems as the feathered dinosaur story. Not every professional paleontologist is convinced about its status as an intermediate form, and recent research has cast further doubt. After all, *Tiktaalik* is one hundred percent fish.

Before *Tiktaalik* appeared on the scene, the best candidate for an intermediate was the fish *Panderichthys*. When *Tiktaalik* was discovered, though, scientists admitted, "*Panderichthys* possesses relatively few tetrapod synapomorphies, and provides only partial insight into the origin of major features of the skull, limbs, and axial skeleton of early tetrapods. In view of the morphological gap between elpistostegalian fish and tetrapods, the phylogenetic framework for the immediate sister group of tetrapods has been incomplete and our understanding of major anatomical transformations at the fish-tetrapod transition has remained limited."[25]

Not only does this comment dethrone *Panderichthys,* it admits that knowledge of the transition from fish to tetrapod has been quite limited. It's interesting to note that no one admitted this lack of knowledge before the discovery of *Tiktaalik.*

Now the story continues. Behind the scenes a variety of scientists have contested *Tiktaalik* as an intermediate. In 2008, a study scanning *Panderichthys* fossils revealed that the bone structure in this fish's fins were closer to those of tetrapods than those of *Tiktaalik.* In an interview with *The Scientist,* study leader Catherine A. Boisvert said, "The disposition of distal radials in *Panderichthys* are much more tetrapodlike than in *Tiktaalik*." She continued, "Previous data from another ancient fish called *Tiktaalik*

The fossil record continues to pose a great challenge to Darwin's theory of evolution.

showed distal radials as well – although the quality of that specimen was poor. And the orientation of the radials did not seem to match the way modern fingers and toes radiate from a joint, parallel to each other."[26]

When *Tiktaalik* was first brought to the public's notice, it was never mentioned that its quality as a fossil specimen was "poor"; instead, *Panderichthys* was dismissed as an intermediate. Now two years later, *Panderichthys* is reclaiming its throne. Yet in *National Geographic,* evolutionary biologist Michael Coates of the University of Chicago was not convinced that the digitlike structures in *Panderichthys's* fins are the equivalent of fingers as we know them. For one thing, he found them unusually flat for radial bones. "Radials are generally cylindrical. When you look at [a] cross-section [of the digits of *Panderichthys*], they're dumbbell-shaped. The structures are so peculiar, they might just be fragments of damaged bone."[27]

So within the two years between 2006 and 2008 we have come to understand that *Panderichthys* does not document a transition from water to land, that *Tiktaalik* is a "poor fossil" and that what have been supposed as tetrapod characteristics could be "fragments of damaged bone." Are the scientists really as convinced about these fossils as the media would have us believe?

While we're on the topic of fish-tetrapod transition, let's not forget the coelacanth. For many years, the fossil fish called *Coelacanth* was said to have been the first fish to walk onto land. This particular species was thought to have legs almost like those of a tetrapod as well as rudimentary lungs. It was also thought that *Coelacanth* lived in shallow waters near land, and became extinct about seventy million years ago.

It therefore came as a great surprise when in 1938 a living specimen of *Coelacanth* was caught in the Indian Ocean off the coast of South Africa. We then learned that this fish, far from being about to take its final step toward becoming a fully land-dwelling animal, was actually a deep-sea fish, never coming closer than 180 meters from the surface. What was assumed to be a developing lung was actually just a fat-filled swimbladder.

There are other examples of alleged transitional forms – evolutionists discuss them in biology textbooks – such as the sequences documenting the evolution of horses and whales. On examination, however, problems similar to the ones above arise.

On the whole, the fossil record continues to pose a great challenge to Darwin's theory of evolution. Contrary to Darwin's expectations, long periods of stasis interrupted by the sudden appearance of completely novel forms is the rule. Intermediate forms rarely appear, and whenever it seems they have, on closer inspection their status as intermediate forms can be seriously contested. As Henry Gee, chief science writer for *Nature*, wrote,

No fossil is buried with its birth certificate ... the intervals of time that separate fossils are so huge that we cannot say anything definite about their possible connection through ancestry and descent ... To take a line of fossils and claim that they represent a lineage is not a scientific hypothesis that can be tested, but an assertion that carries the same validity as a bedtime story – amusing, perhaps even instructive, but not scientific.[28]

Anomalous Fossil Evidence

On a final note, we will briefly touch on the fact that a number of anomalous fossils have been gathered that contradict the standard Darwinian account of evolution. Arguably, the best-known collection of anomalous human fossils – fossils that reveal the presence of anatomically modern humans tens of millions of years earlier than has been thought possible – has been presented by Michael Cremo and Richard Thompson [see chapter 9]. This evidence stands in stark contrast to the standard Darwinian account, in which modern humans appeared only within the last 100,000 to 200,000 years.

One has to wonder whether similarly anomalous evidence has been found for nonhuman species. It seems there is such evidence, but it is scanty. Perhaps the best known cases are those of the anomalous remains of flowering plants found in layers of rock much older than the accepted age for such plants. In the 1960s, scientists reported finding flower pollen and spores in Precambrian rock formations in Venezuela and British Guyana that dated between 1.7 and 2 billion years old.[29] According to current theory, flowering plants evolved fairly recently – only 100 million years ago.

Also, in 1956, S. Leclercq, a paleontologist from the University of Liege, Belgium, cited a number of similar cases. In a review article in the journal *Evolution,* she discussed fossil evidence from around the world, including Siberia and Canada, of higher plants found in strata belonging to an age in which flowering plants are supposed to have not yet evolved.[30]

From the middle of the nineteenth century to the middle of the twentieth century, a controversy raged about the age of the saline layers in what is known as the Salt Range Mountains of Pakistan. Geologists generally regarded these layers as Cambrian and Precambrian – that is, as more than 600 million years old. They came to this conclusion because the saline layers are effectively covered by what is known as Cambrian purple sandstone. It seemed natural, then, to assume that the underlying salt formations are Precambrian. Modern geologists agree with this assumption.

However, paleontologists came to contest this date when they found microfossils of insects and flowering plants in the saline rocks. One such challenger was Professor B. Sahni, who considered the layers Eocene (about 55 million years old) because according to standard evolutionary theory these fossils could not have been formed earlier than that. At one point during the controversy geologist E. R. Gee posited that more advanced flora and fauna existed during the Cambrian. His theory was summarily dismissed, of course, but it is worth noting that while it challenged the evolutionary status quo, it provided the most direct interpretation of the different lines of evidence.[31]

This controversy died out in the 1950s, although it was never satisfactorily resolved, and some scientists continue to explore the possibility that flowering plants existed in Precambrian times. For example, Professor Amiya Kumar Ghosh (1905–1985) from the Botany department of Calcutta University said openly during the Salt Range controversy that he was willing to consider the possibility that higher plant forms existed earlier than usually thought. After Sahni's death in 1949, Ghosh felt inspired to conduct further research. In the 1950s and '60s he investigated several Cambrian and Precambrian sites in India, such as those in the Punjab Salt Range and others in the Vindhya Mountains. He also researched several sites in North America. During his research he was able to extract wood remains and spores from higher plants, supporting his earlier guess that higher plants had actually existed in the Precambrian. He discussed his findings in 1973 at a lecture at the Bose Institute in Calcutta. His lecture caught the ear of scientists worldwide and he became known as "Cambrian Ghosh."[32]

In conclusion, anomalous fossil evidence does exist, but it is sparse. Perhaps there are so few examples because almost no one is looking for it. The mainstream scientific community does not encourage investigation into ideas that have the potential to radically alter their theories' status quo, and scientists convinced about standard Darwinian theory are unlikely to search for fossil evidence that contradicts it – evidence they think shouldn't exist. Whenever such evidence *has* occasionally surfaced, much energy has been devoted to accounting for it within the current theoretical paradigm. Hardly anyone considers that perhaps the current theory is mistaken.

CHAPTER 4

What is Intelligent Design?

William A. Dembski

A ccording to Darwinism, undirected natural causes are solely responsible for the origin and development of life. In particular, Darwinism rules out the possibility of God or any guiding intelligence playing a role in life's origin and development. Within Western culture Darwinism's ascent has been truly meteoric. And yet throughout its ascent there have always been dissenters who regarded as inadequate the Darwinian vision that undirected natural causes could produce the full diversity and complexity of life.

Until the mid 1980s this dissent was sporadic and completely marginalized. With the subsequent rise of the Intelligent Design movement, this dissent has now become focused within the intellectual and scientific worlds, promising to overturn the cultural dominance of Darwinism much as the freedom movements in Eastern Europe overturned the political dominance of Marxism at the end of the 1980s.

The Intelligent Design movement begins with the work of Charles Thaxton, Walter Bradley, Michael Denton, Dean Kenyon, and Phillip Johnson. Without employing the Bible as a scientific text, these scholars critiqued Darwinism on scientific and philosophical grounds. On scientific grounds they found Darwinism an inadequate framework for biology. On philosophical grounds they found Darwinism hopelessly entangled with naturalism, the view that nature is self-sufficient and thus without need of God or any guiding intelligence. With the publication of Michael Behe's *Darwin's Black Box* (1996) and my own *The Design Inference* (1998), the Intelligent Design community has coalesced and taken the next step, proposing a positive research program in which intelligent causation (and especially intelligently devised information) becomes the key for understanding the diversity and complexity of life.

Through this two-pronged approach of critiquing Darwinism on the one hand and providing a positive alternative on the other, the Intelligent Design movement has rapidly gained adherents among the best and brightest in the academy. Already it is responsible for Darwinism losing its corner on the intellectual market. If fully successful, Intelligent Design will unseat not just Darwinism but also Darwinism's cultural legacy. And since no aspect of Western culture has escaped Darwinism's influence, so no aspect of Western culture will escape reevaluation in the light of Intelligent Design.

What is Intelligent Design?

What then is Intelligent Design? Intelligent Design begins with the observation that intelligent causes can do things which undirected natural causes cannot. Undirected natural causes can place scrabble pieces on a board, but cannot arrange the pieces as meaningful words or sentences. To obtain a meaningful arrangement requires an intelligent cause.

This intuition, that there is a fundamental distinction between undirected natural causes on the one hand and intelligent causes

Scrabble. When seeing letters arranged into meaningful words everyone knows that an intelligent designer was at play.

on the other, has underlain the design arguments of past centuries. Throughout the centuries theologians have argued that nature exhibits features which nature itself cannot explain but which instead require an intelligence over and above nature. From Church fathers like Minucius Felix and Basil the Great (3rd and 4th centuries) to medieval scholastics like Moses Maimonides and Thomas Aquinas (12th and 13th centuries) to reformed thinkers like Thomas Reid and Charles Hodge (18th and 19th centuries), we find theologians making design arguments, arguing from the data of nature to an intelligence operating over and above nature. Design arguments are thus old hat, and indeed continue to be a staple of philosophy and religion courses.

The most famous of the design arguments is William Paley's watchmaker argument (as in Paley's *Natural Theology*, published 1802). According to Paley, if we find a watch in a field, the watch's adaptation of means to ends (that is, the adaptation of its parts to telling time) ensure that it is the product of an intelligence and not simply the output of undirected natural processes. So too the marvelous adaptations of means to ends in organisms, whether at the level of whole organisms or at the level of various subsystems (Paley focused especially on the mammalian eye), ensure that organisms are the product of an intelligence.

William Paley argued that if one found a watch lying on the ground, one would immediately conclude it was made by someone. Similarly, the complex organs of living organisms, such as the eye, also suggest an intelligent cause.

Though intuitively appealing, Paley's argument had until recently fallen into disuse. In the absence of precise methods for distinguishing intelligently caused objects from unintelligently caused ones, the scientific mainstream over the last hundred and fifty years simply ignored the concept of design. For design to be a fruitful scientific concept, scientists have to be sure they can reliably determine whether something is designed. The German astronomer Johannes Kepler (1571–1630) thought the craters on the moon were intelligently designed by moon dwellers. We now know that the craters were formed naturally. It's this fear of falsely attributing something to design only to have it overturned later that has prevented design from entering science proper.

This fear of falsely attributing design so infects the biological community that for more than a century it has insisted that living things be explained apart from design. To be sure, the term "design" is everywhere in the biological literature. But what is meant is the mere appearance of design. According to the biological community, the appearance of design in biology must not be confused with its reality. This is not to deny that biology is filled with marvelous contrivances. Biologists readily admit as much. But as far as the biological community is concerned, living things are not the result of a purposeful design process. Thus Oxford biologist Richard Dawkins writes, "Biology is the study of complicated things that give the appearance of having been designed for a purpose." Likewise, Nobel laureate Francis Crick writes, "Biologists must constantly keep in mind that what they see was not designed, but rather evolved."

How does the biological community know that living things are only apparently and not actually designed? The exclusion of design from biology certainly contrasts with the experience from ordinary life where what appears to be designed for the most part actually is so. But from the perspective of biology as a natural science, design, as the action of an intelligent agent, is not a fundamental creative force in nature. Rather, blind natural causes, characterized by chance and necessity and ruled by unbroken laws, are thought sufficient to do all nature's creating.

This is where Darwin's theory comes in. According to Darwinist Francisco Ayala, "The functional design of organisms and their features would therefore seem to argue for the existence of a designer. It was Darwin's greatest accomplishment to show that the directive organization of living beings can be explained as the result of a natural process, natural selection, without any need to resort to a Creator or other external agent. The origin and adaptation of organisms in their profusion and wondrous variations were thus brought into the realm of science."

But is it really the case that the directive organization of living beings can be explained without recourse to a designer? And would employing a designer in biological explanations necessarily take us out of the realm of science? The answer to both questions is No. With the start of the 1990s, design has witnessed an explosive resurgence. Scientists are beginning to realize that design can be rigorously formulated as a scientific theory. With precise methods for discriminating intelligently from unintelligently caused objects, scientists are now able to avoid Kepler's mistake. What has emerged is a new program for scientific research known as Intelligent Design.

Detecting Intelligent Design

Within biology, Intelligent Design is a theory of biological origins and development. Its fundamental claim is that intelligent causes are necessary to explain the complex, information-rich structures of biology, and that these causes are empirically detectable. To say intelligent causes are empirically detectable is to say there exist well-defined methods that, on the basis of observational features of the world, are capable of reliably distinguishing intelligent causes from undirected natural causes.

Many special sciences have already developed such methods for drawing this distinction – notably forensic science, cryptography, archeology, random-number generation, and the Search for Extraterrestrial Intelligence. Whenever these methods detect intelligent causation, the underlying entity they uncover is a type of information known alternately as *specified complexity* or *complex specified information*.

For instance, how did the radio astronomers in the movie *Contact* (a movie starring Jodie Foster and based on a novel by Carl Sagan) infer the presence of extraterrestrial intelligence in the radio signals they monitored from space? The researchers ran signals through computers that were programmed to recognize many preset patterns. These patterns act as a sieve. Signals that do not match any of the patterns pass through the sieve and are classified as random.

According to the movie, after years of receiving apparently meaningless random signals, the *Contact* researchers discover a pattern of beats and pauses that corresponds to the sequence of all the prime numbers between 2 and 101. (Prime numbers are numbers divisible only by themselves and by one.) When a sequence begins with two beats, then a pause, three beats, then a pause ... and continues all the way to 101 beats, researchers must infer the presence of an extraterrestrial intelligence.

Why? There is nothing in the laws of physics that requires radio signals to take one form or another. The sequence is therefore *contingent* rather than necessary. Also, it is a long sequence and therefore *complex*. Note that if the sequence lacked complexity, it could easily have happened by chance. Finally, it was not just complex but also exhibited an independently given pattern or *specification* (it was not just any old sequence of numbers but a mathematically significant one – the prime numbers).

Specified complexity's causal chains end not with nature but with a designing intelligence.

To summarize, an event exhibits specified complexity if it is contingent and therefore not necessary; if it is complex and therefore not easily reproducible by chance; and if it is specified in the sense of exhibiting an independently given pattern. Note that complexity in the sense of improbability is not sufficient to eliminate chance – flip a coin long enough and you will witness a highly complex or improbable event. Even so, you will have no reason not to attribute it to chance.

The important thing about specifications is that they be objectively given and not just imposed on events after the fact. For instance, if an archer fires arrows into a wall and then paints bull's-eyes around the arrows, the archer imposes a pattern after the fact. On the other hand, if the targets are set up in advance (specified), and then the archer hits them accurately, we know it was due to the archer's intelligent action – in other words, to design.

The combination of complexity and specification convincingly pointed the radio astronomers in *Contact* to an extraterrestrial intelligence. Specified complexity is the characteristic trademark or signature of intelligence. Specified complexity is a reliable empirical marker of intelligence in the same way that fingerprints are a reliable empirical marker of a person's presence (for the theoretical justification see my book *No Free Lunch*, 2002).

Only intelligent causation gives rise to specified complexity. Accordingly, specified complexity lies beyond the capacity of blind natural causes to generate it. This is not to say that naturally occurring systems cannot exhibit specified complexity or that natural processes cannot serve as a conduit for specified complexity. That is not the point. The point is whether nature (conceived as a closed system of blind, unbroken natural causes) can *generate* specified complexity in the sense of originating it when previously there was none.

To see what is at stake, consider a Dürer woodcut. It arose by mechanically impressing an inked woodblock on paper. The Dürer woodcut exhibits specified complexity. But the mechanical application of ink to paper via a woodblock does not account for that specified complexity in the woodcut. The specified complexity in the woodcut must be referred back to the specified complexity in the woodblock which in turn must be referred back to the designing activity of Dürer himself (in this case deliberately chiseling the woodblock). Specified complexity's causal chains end not with nature but with a designing intelligence.

The actual term *specified complexity* is not original with me. It first occurs in the origin-of-life literature, where Leslie Orgel used it to describe what he regards as the essence of life. That was thirty years ago. More recently, in 1999, surveying the state of origin-of-life research, Paul Davies remarked: "Living organisms are mysterious not for their complexity *per se* but for their tightly specified complexity."[1] Orgel and Davies used specified complexity loosely. In my own research I've formalized it as a statistical criterion for identifying the effects of intelligence.

When properly formulated, the theory of intelligent design is a mathematical theory of information. Within such a theory, complex specified information (or specified complexity) becomes a reliable indicator of intelligent causation as well as a proper object for scientific investigation. The theory of intelligent design thereby becomes a theory for detecting and measuring information, explaining its origin, and tracing its flow. The theory of intelligent design therefore does not study intelligent causes per se but the informational pathways induced by intelligent causes. As a result, the theory of intelligent design presupposes neither a creator nor miracles. The theory of intelligent design is theologically minimalist. It detects intelligence without speculating about the nature of the intelligence.

Biochemist Michael Behe (*Darwin's Black Box,* 1996) connects specified complexity to biological design. Behe defines a system as *irreducibly complex* if it consists of several interrelated parts so that removing even one part completely destroys the system's function. For Behe, irreducible complexity is a sure indicator of design. One irreducibly complex biochemical system that Behe considers is the bacterial flagellum. The flagellum is an acid-powered rotary motor with a whip-like tail that spins at 20,000 rpm (revolutions per minute) and whose rotating motion enables a bacterium to navigate through its watery environment.

Behe shows that the intricate machinery in this molecular motor – including a rotor, a stator, O-rings, bushings, and a drive shaft – requires the coordinated interaction of at least thirty complex proteins, and that the absence of any one of these proteins would result in the complete loss of motor function. Behe argues that such irreducibly complex systems are beyond the reach of the Darwinian mechanism. It can be shown that Behe's notion of irreducible complexity is a special case of specified complexity and that systems like the bacterial flagellum exhibit specified complexity and are therefore designed (see *The Design of Life,* by Jonathan Wells and me).

In applying the test of specified complexity to biological organisms, design theorists focus on identifiable systems – such as individual enzymes, molecular machines, and the like – that exhibit a clear function and for which complexity can be reasonably assessed. Of course, once specified complexity is exhibited by some part of an organism, then any design attributable to that part carries over to the whole organism. It is not necessary to demonstrate that every aspect of the whole organism is the result of design. Some aspects will be the result of chance or necessity.

Design has had a turbulent intellectual history. The chief difficulty with design to date has consisted in discovering a conceptually powerful formulation of it that will fruitfully advance science. This has now been achieved. The empirical detectability of intelligent causes makes intelligent design a full-fledged scientific theory and distinguishes it from the design arguments of philosophers and theologians, or what has traditionally been called "natural theology."

The world contains events, objects, and structures that exhaust the explanatory resources of undirected natural causes and that can be adequately explained only by recourse to intelligent causes. The theory of intelligent design demonstrates this rigorously. It thus takes a long-standing philosophical intuition and transforms it into a scientific research program.

The implications of intelligent design for religious belief are profound. The rise of modern science led to a vigorous attack on all religions that treat purpose, intelligence, and wisdom as fundamental and irreducible features of reality. The high point of this attack came with Darwin's theory of evolution. The central claim of Darwin's theory is that an unguided material process (random variation and natural selection) could account for the emergence of all biological complexity and order. In other words, Darwin appeared to show that the design in biology (and, by implication, in nature generally) was dispensable. By showing that design is indispensable to the scientific understanding of the natural world, intelligent design is reinvigorating the design argument. At the same time, it is overturning the widespread misconception that the only tenable form of religious belief is one that treats purpose, intelligence, and wisdom as by-products of unintelligent material processes. No, design is fundamental!

CHAPTER 5

Convergence

"To suppose that the eye with all its inimitable contrivances for adjusting the focus to different distances, for admitting different amounts of light, and for the correction of spherical and chromatic aberration, could have been formed by natural selection, seems, I freely confess, absurd in the highest degree."[1]

The "camera eye" of mammals and a number of other creatures is one of the most complex organs they possess. Therefore the difficulty Charles Darwin expressed in accounting for it through the processes of natural selection is understandable. The eye is astoundingly intricate, with its cornea, retina, pupil, iris, optic nerve, and other structures set in a coordinated and irreducible interaction. The eye contains certain transparent cells that are found nowhere else in the body. The biochemistry of vision – something Darwin did not understand, since science hadn't advanced to the point of analyzing it yet – is a world of its own, with dozens of complex proteins cascading to set off electric signals in the brain whenever a photon hits the retina.

How could such a structure have evolved through a sequence of gradual but random changes, from the light-sensitive spot of a primitive creature to a fully developed mammalian eye? This would be like going from a simple slide projector to a high-definition color television by mere successive modifications of design and without losing function at any stage. Yet this is what the theory of evolution claims happened in regards to the eye. To accept the evolutionists' claim as true science, we would require detailed models of exactly how each transitional stage worked. Unfortunately, no such thing has been put forward.

And the problem doesn't stop there. Have you ever looked a squid in the eye? The eye structure of humans (and vertebrates in general) is highly similar to the eye structure of squids, yet it is supposed by evolutionary theory that the last ancestor shared by humans and squids possessed no eyes. This means, according to the theory of evolution, that the complex structure of a camera eye evolved more than once. This brings us to the topic of convergence.

When similar structures are considered the result of common descent, evolutionists call them "homologous"; when similar structures cannot be explained by common descent, the structures are considered "convergent." Nature is full of apparent convergence. For example, powered flight, according to evolutionists, has arisen independently at least four times in the animal kingdom: in birds, in bats, in flying reptiles (pterosaurs), and in insects. None of the supposed common ancestors between these species possessed either wings or the ability to fly.

According to the theory of evolution, flight has arisen independently at least four times in birds, insects, bats, and pterosaurs.

Evolutionists claim that vision has independently developed more than forty separate times, and specifically, the cameralike eye design has arisen at least nine times. Cambridge professor Simon Conway Morris, who discusses convergence extensively in his 2003 book *Life's Solution*, calls this much convergent evolution "eerie."[2]

Another striking example of convergence is the panda's thumb. All pandas have an extra digit on their forelimbs along with the five normal vertebrate fingers. This extra digit is actually a modified wrist bone, and it enables the pandas to hold bamboo shoots while eating them. There are two kinds of pandas, the giant panda and the red panda, and they both have this extra thumb. Now, contrary to what one would assume on the face of it, according to present evolutionary understanding the last common ancestor between these two types of pandas did not possess this thumb. After decades of discussion, biologists now classify the two pandas in distinct families, and thus their peculiar thumb is considered an instance of convergence.

Convergence is particularly evident in the case of placentals and marsupials. Marsupials live mainly in Australia. Dozens of placentals – almost all mammals are placentals – have near-identical species among the marsupials, although the two groups are supposed to have evolved independently of one another. Mice, moles, squirrels, and numerous other placental mammals have marsupial counterparts. Their similarities are striking. Consider the Tasmanian wolf, extinct now since the 1930s. This marsupial predator was completely unrelated to wolves and other canine species of the Northern hemisphere, yet it was strikingly similar in a number of ways: its

Tasmanian wolf and common wolf, supposedly an instance of convergent evolution.

overall body shape, its sharp teeth, powerful jaws, paws, and gait. Its fur was striped like a tiger's, which does distinguish it from canines, but skeletally it is almost identical to a canine. Placed side by side, the craniums of the Tasmanian wolf and the common placental wolf are almost indistinguishable (see picture).

Convergence is not restricted to morphological characteristics; it is also found at the embryological level and at the molecular level. But although convergence is widespread, with countless examples everywhere one looks in the living world, the issue hasn't received as much attention from biologists as it deserves. Morris was probably the first evolutionary biologist to deal extensively with it, in his *Life's Solution*, which, although by no means exhaustive, offers a large catalogue of instances of convergence.

Evolutionists seem uncomfortable with the abundance of convergence in nature and seldom focus public attention on it. Perhaps this is because it's so hard to explain. Convergence is not due to common descent, nor, moreover, is it due to other evolutionary mechanisms – lateral gene transfer, for example. Here it is again good to bear in mind that in nature examples of convergent evolution do not produce identical structures but only structures (or organisms) that are highly similar. If they had been identical, evolutionists might have been able to attribute them to lateral gene transfer or some other form of complete transferal of complex genetic traits from one organism to another. But a genetic transferal is not possible to invoke when the convergences are not identical but only highly similar. Thus evolutionists are left with a not very desirable explanation – the *separate and independent evolution* of numerous highly similar complex biological traits.

This goes against common evolutionary wisdom. Being random and unguided, evolution is certainly not expected to repeat itself. As put by the famous British evolutionary biologist John Maynard Smith, "If one was able to replay the whole evolution of animals, starting at the bottom of the Cambrian, there is no guarantee – indeed no likelihood – that the result would be the same. There might be no conquest of the land, no emergence of mammals, and certainly no human beings."[3] But according to evolutionists, convergence is precisely that: evolution time and time again coming up with similar results.

Simon Conway Morris circumvents this in a peculiar way in *Life's*

Solution. He asserts at the outset that evolution is an already established fact not to be argued with – "Evolution is true; it happens"[4] – and therefore the numerous convergences so brilliantly discussed in his book *must* be the result of evolution; indeed, according to Morris, not only is convergence no problem for evolution but strong evidence of its astounding powers. Of course, someone less convinced about evolution than Dr. Morris might consider his logic circular. That is, he appears to be proving an assumption by using as evidence the assumption itself. In a discussion of whether evolution happened in the first place it seems highly unsatisfactory to prove the reality of evolution by assuming it to be true.

Morris goes so far as to claim that highly similar convergent traits "provide no comfort for 'creation scientists' because in their various ways they provide compelling evidence of the reality of organic evolution."[5] Unfortunately, he doesn't elaborate on how he arrived at this conclusion. The only implied logic that I can detect is that he apparently finds it self-evident that a creator would never create convergent features like this. In other words, according to Morris, a creator should be expected to create identical features and not only highly similar features. Such features must, therefore, by implication, be the result of an accidental unguided evolution.

This is, of course, unsatisfactory. First, Morris doesn't specify a mechanism that can account for how highly similar features can arise independently of one another again and again. Second, arguments about what a creator would or would not do belong to theology. For evolutionary biologists to base their arguments for evolution on theological notions, although, in fact, less common, is improper. For Morris to resort to theological arguments in a discussion of biology shows how inconvenient the numerous instances of convergence in nature are for the theory of evolution.[*]

One researcher, Walter ReMine, turns this particular theological

---

[*] See this book's last chapter for more discussion on the abundance of theological claims made by evolutionary biologists.

argument on its head and claims that the creator has deliberately placed highly similar but not identical convergent traits everywhere in nature to defy any evolutionary explanation.[6] If these convergent traits had been completely identical they could have been explained in other ways and strengthened the case for evolution, but this becomes impossible when they are only highly similar. And since the repeated independent evolution of very similar traits through a random, unguided process defies all probability, the only explanation left is intelligent design. Thus, ReMine says, the convergences found in nature are deliberately placed by the creator to point to his existence.

Another possibility might be that a creator is creating variations over the same themes, as composers of music and artists often do. Perhaps the creator is not a prosaic and minimalistic creator, whose work of creation has to be as functionalistic and cost efficient as possible. Perhaps he in reality has a sense of aestheticism and beauty and enjoys unfolding his artistic abilities through his creative work in nature.

Whether any of these theological speculations are true is beyond the scope of this book; I mention them only to prove that the theological speculations of evolutionary biologists are not the only possible theological speculations. Strictly speaking, none of them belong in a discussion on science. Neither do any of them make an evolutionary explanation for the many instances of convergence in nature more likely.

CHAPTER 6

Irreducible Complexity: Obstacle to Darwinian Evolution

Michael J. Behe

A Sketch of the Intelligent Design Hypothesis

In his seminal work *On The Origin of Species,* Darwin hoped to explain what no one had been able to explain before – how the variety and complexity of the living world might have been produced by simple natural laws. His idea for doing so was, of course, the theory of evolution by natural selection. In a nutshell, Darwin saw that there was variety in all species. For example, some members of a species are bigger than others, some faster, some brighter in color. He knew that not all organisms that were born would survive to reproduce, simply because there was not enough food to sustain them all. So Darwin reasoned that the ones whose chance variation gave them an edge in the struggle for life would tend to survive and leave offspring. If the variation could be inherited, then over time the characteristics of the species would change, and over great periods of time, perhaps great changes could occur.

It was an elegant idea, and many scientists of the time quickly saw that it could explain many things about biology. However, there

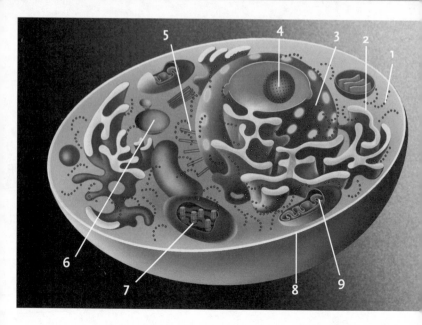

remained an important reason for reserving judgment about whether it could actually account for all of biology: the basis of life was yet unknown. In Darwin's day atoms and molecules were still theoretical constructs – no one was sure if such things actually existed. Many scientists of Darwin's era took the cell to be a simple glob of protoplasm, something like a microscopic piece of Jell-O. Thus the intricate molecular basis of life was utterly unknown to Darwin and his contemporaries.

In the past hundred years science has learned much more about the cell and, especially in the past fifty years, much about the molecular basis of life. The discoveries of the double helical structure of DNA, the genetic code, the complicated, irregular structure of proteins, and much else have given us a greater appreciation for the elaborate structures that are necessary to sustain life. Indeed, we have seen that the cell is run by machines – literally, machines made of molecules. There are molecular machines that enable the cell to move, machines that

In Darwin's time living cells were regarded as simple, small drops of jelly. However, over the last fifty years, scientists have uncovered inside the cell a marvel of complexity, which is not found anywhere else in nature. The origination of this has so far eluded the biochemists. Some important structures of typical plant and animal cells are depicted in this illustration.

1. *The ribosomes manufacture protein molecules by following blueprints encoded in messenger RNA. Although they appear here as mere dots, the ribosomes have a complex structure.*

2. *The endoplasmic reticulum consists of a complex of membranes that form internal compartments used in the synthesis and transport of various compounds produced by the cell.*

3. *The nucleus contains the hereditary material, DNA, which carries instructions for the operation and perpetuation of the cellular machinery. Complex molecular processes are involved in replicating the DNA.*

4. *The nucleolus is a factory for the partial manufacture of ribosomes.*

5. *The microtubules form a complex latticework that gives form to the cell and enables it to systematically move and change shape.*

6. *Lysosomes contain enzymes that break down unwanted material within the cell.*

7. *The chloroplasts found in plant cells are complex chemical factories that carry out photosynthesis – the storage of solar energy in the form of sugar molecules.*

8. *The cellular membrane is equipped with many complex protein molecules that regulate the passage of molecules into and out of the cell and act as sensors informing the cell of external conditions.*

9. *The mitochondria are chemical factories that generate energy for the cell through the controlled breakdown of food molecules.*

empower it to transport nutrients, machines that allow it to defend itself.

In light of the enormous progress made by science since Darwin first proposed his theory, it is reasonable to ask if the theory still seems to be a good explanation for life. In *Darwin's Black Box: The Biochemical Challenge to Evolution*,[1] I argued that it is not. The main difficulty for Darwinian mechanisms is that many systems in the cell are what I termed "irreducibly complex." I defined an irreducibly complex system as a single system which is necessarily composed of several well-matched, interacting parts that contribute to the basic function, and where the removal of any one of the parts causes the system to effectively cease functioning.[2] As an example of an irreducibly complex system from everyday life, I pointed to a mechanical mousetrap such as one finds in a hardware store. Typically such traps have a number of parts: a spring, wooden platform, hammer, and other pieces. If one removes a piece from the trap, it can't catch mice. Without the spring, or hammer, or the other pieces, one doesn't have a trap that works half as well as it used to, or a quarter as well; one has a broken mousetrap, which doesn't work at all.

Irreducibly complex systems seem very difficult to fit into a Darwinian framework, for a reason insisted on by Darwin himself. In *Origin* Darwin wrote that "If it could be demonstrated that any complex organ existed which could not possibly have been formed by numerous, successive, slight modifications, my theory would absolutely break down. But I can find out no such case."[3] Here Darwin was emphasizing that his was a gradual theory. Natural selection had to improve systems by tiny steps, over a long period of time, because if things improved too rapidly, or in large steps, then it would begin to look as if something other than natural selection was driving the process. However, it is hard to see how something like a mousetrap could arise gradually by something akin to a Darwinian process. For example, a spring by itself or a platform by itself would not catch mice, and adding a piece to the first nonfunctioning piece wouldn't make a trap either. So it appears that irreducibly complex biological systems would present a considerable obstacle to Darwinian evolution.

The question then becomes, Are there any irreducibly complex systems in the cell? Are there any irreducibly complex molecular machines? Yes, there are many. In *Darwin's Black Box* I discussed several biochemical systems as examples of irreducible complexity: the eukaryotic cilium; the intracellular transport system; and more. Here I will just briefly describe the bacterial flagellum,[4] since its structure makes the difficulty for Darwinian evolution easy to see (Figure 1). The flagellum can be thought of as an outboard motor that bacteria use to swim. It was the first truly rotary structure discovered in nature. It consists of a long filamentous tail that acts as a propeller; when it is spun it pushes against the liquid medium and can propel the bacterium forward. The propeller is attached to the drive shaft indirectly through something called the hook region, which acts as a universal joint. The drive shaft is attached to the motor, which uses a flow of acid or sodium ions from the outside of the cell to the inside to power rotation. Just as an outboard motor has to be kept stationary on a motorboat while

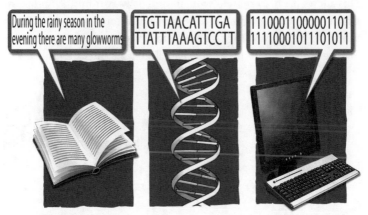

The information DNA contains can no more be reduced to chemistry than the ideas in a book can be reduced to paper and ink, or the software in a computer be the result of processes in the medium onto which it is stored, the hardware.

the propeller turns, there are proteins that act as a stator structure to keep the flagellum in place. Other proteins act as bushings to permit the drive shaft to pass through the bacterial membrane. Studies have shown that 30 to 40 proteins are required to produce a functioning flagellum in the cell. About half of the proteins are components of the finished structure, while the others are necessary for the construction of the flagellum. In the absence of almost any of the proteins – in the absence of the parts that act as the propeller, drive shaft, hook, and so forth – no functioning flagellum is built.

As with the mousetrap, it is quite difficult to see how Darwin's gradualistic process of natural selection sieving random mutations could produce the bacterial flagellum, since many pieces are required before its function appears. A hook by itself or drive shaft by itself will not act as a propulsive device. But the situation is actually much worse than it appears from this cursory description for several reasons. First, there is associated with the functioning of the flagellum an intricate control system, which tells the flagellum when to rotate, when to stop, and sometimes when to reverse itself and rotate in the opposite direction. This allows the bacterium to swim toward or away from an appropriate signal rather than in a random direction which could much more easily take it the wrong way. Thus the problem of accounting for the origin of the flagellum is not limited to the flagellum itself but extends to associated control systems as well.

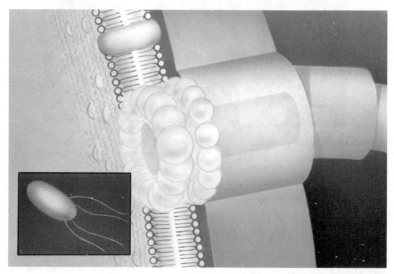

Figure 1

Second, a more subtle problem is how the parts assemble themselves into a whole. The analogy of an outboard motor fails in one respect: an outboard motor is generally assembled under the direction of a human – an intelligent agent that can specify which parts are attached to which other parts. The information for assembling a bacterial flagellum, however (or indeed all other biomolecular machines), resides in the component proteins of the structure itself. Recent work shows that the assembly process for a flagellum is exceedingly elegant and intricate.[5] If that assembly information is absent from the proteins, then no flagellum is produced. Thus even if we had a hypothetical cell in which proteins homologous to all of the parts of the flagellum were present (perhaps performing jobs other than propulsion), but were missing the information on how to assemble themselves into a flagellum, we would still not get the structure. The problem of irreducibility would remain.

Because of such considerations, I have concluded that Darwinian processes are not promising explanations for many biochemical systems in the cell. Instead I have noted that if one looks at the interactions of the components of the flagellum or cilium or other irreducibly complex cellular systems, they look like they were designed – purposely designed by an intelligent agent. The features of the systems that indicate design are the same ones that stymie Darwinian explanations: the specific interaction of multiple components to accomplish a function which is beyond the individual components. The logical structure of the argument to design is a simple inductive one: whenever we see such highly specific interactions in our everyday world, whether in a mousetrap or elsewhere, we unfailingly find that the systems were intentionally arranged – that they were designed. Now we find systems of similar complexity in the cell. Since no other explanation has successfully addressed them, I argue we should extend the induction to subsume molecular machines and hypothesize that they were purposely designed.

Misconceptions About What a Hypothesis of Design Entails

The hypothesis of intelligent design (ID) is quite controversial, mostly because of its philosophical and theological overtones, and in the years since *Darwin's Black Box* was published a number of scientists and philosophers have tried to refute its main argument. I have found these rebuttals unpersuasive at best. Quite the opposite, I think that some putative counterexamples to design are unintentionally instructive in that not only do they fail to make their case for the sufficiency of natural selection but they show clearly the obstacle that irreducible complexity poses to Darwinism. They also show that Darwinists have great

This sketch shows the action of an enzyme called DNA topoisomerase, which gives another glimpse into irreducible complex systems inside the cell. During cellular reproduction, the DNA double helix molecule separates into two helixes. As the upper portion of the helix uncoils, it causes the lower portion to wind upon itself, or supercoil. Since the DNA is already folded hundreds of times to fit in the cell, supercoiling invariably causes the strands to tangle. This tangling would prohibit reproduction; therefore the cell activates an enzyme, DNA topoisomerase, that unravels the knots in the DNA strands. The topoimerase rearranges the DNA strands as follows. First it cuts one of the overlapping strands, then pulls the other strand through the opening, and finally joins the ends of the cut strand back together. By means of this highly sophisticated operation, the DNA topoisomerase sorts out the DNA tangles.

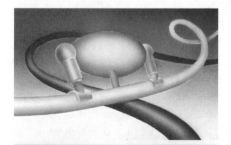
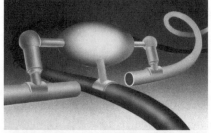
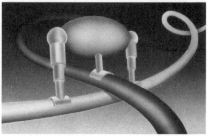

trouble recognizing problems for their own theory. I will examine two of those counterexamples in detail a little later in this chapter. Before I do, however, I will first address a few common misconceptions that surround the biochemical design argument.

First of all, it is important to understand that a hypothesis of intelligent design has no quarrel with evolution per se – that is, "evolution" understood simply as descent with modification, but leaving the mechanism open. After all, a designer may have chosen to work that way. Rather than common descent, the focus of ID is on the *mechanism* of evolution – how did all this happen, by natural selection or by purposeful intelligent design?

A second point that is often overlooked but should be emphasized is that intelligent design can happily coexist with even a large degree of natural selection. Antibiotic and pesticide resistance, antifreeze proteins in fish and plants, and more may indeed be explained by a Darwinian mechanism. The critical claim of ID is not that natural selection doesn't explain *anything* but that it doesn't explain *everything*.

My book, *Darwin's Black Box,* in which I flesh out the design argument, has been widely discussed in many publications. Although many issues have been raised, I think the general reaction by scientists to the design argument is well and succinctly summarized in a recent book, *The Way of the Cell,* published by Oxford University Press and authored by Colorado State University biochemist Franklin Harold. Citing my book Harold writes, "We should reject, as a matter of principle, the substitution of intelligent design for the dialogue of chance and necessity (Behe 1996); but we must concede that there are presently no detailed Darwinian accounts of the evolution of any biochemical system, only a variety of wishful speculations."[6]

Let me emphasize in reverse order Harold's two points. First, as other reviewers of my book have done,[7] he acknowledges that Darwinists have no real explanations for the enormous complexity of the cell, only hand-waving speculations more colloquially known as "Just-So stories." I had claimed essentially the same thing six years earlier in *Darwin's Black Box* and encountered fierce resistance – mostly from internet fans of Darwinism who claimed that, why, there were hundreds of thousands of research papers describing the Darwinian evolution of irreducibly complex biochemical systems, and who set up web sites to document them.[8]

As a sufficient response to such claims I will simply rely on Harold's statement quoted here, as well as the other reviewers who agree that there is a dearth of Darwinian explanations. After all, if prominent scientists who are no fans of intelligent design agree that the systems remain unexplained, then that should settle the matter. Let me pause, however, to note that I find this an astonishing admission for a theory that has dominated biology for so long. That Darwinian theory has borne such little fruit in explaining the molecular basis of life – despite its long reign as the fundamental theory of biology – strongly suggests that it is not the right framework to understanding the origin of the complexity of life.

Harold's second point is that he apparently thinks there is some principle that forbids us from investigating intelligent design, even though design is an obvious idea that quickly pops into your mind when you see a drawing of the flagellum (Figure 1) or other complex biochemical systems. What principle is that? He never spells it out, but I think the principle likely boils down to this: Design appears to point strongly beyond nature. It has philosophical and theological implications, and that makes many people uncomfortable. They think that science should avoid a theory that points so strongly beyond nature, and so they want to rule out intelligent design from the start.

I completely disagree with that view and find it fainthearted. I think science should follow the evidence wherever it seems to lead. That is the only way to make progress. Furthermore, it is not only intelligent design, but *any* theory that purports to explain how life occurred will have philosophical and theological implications. For example, the Oxford biologist Richard Dawkins has famously said that "Darwin made it possible to be an intellectually fulfilled atheist."[9] A little less famously, Kenneth Miller has written that "[God] used evolution as the tool to set us free."[10] Stuart Kauffman, a leading complexity theorist, thinks Darwinism cannot explain all of biology: "Darwinism is not enough ... [N]atural selection cannot be the sole source of order we see in the world."[11] But he thinks that his theory will somehow show that we are "at home in the universe." The point, then, is that all theories of origins carry philosophical and theological implications. There is no way to avoid them in an explanation of life.

Another source of difficulty for some people concerns the question, How could biochemical systems have been designed? A common misconception is that designed systems would have to be created from scratch in a puff of smoke. But that isn't necessarily so. The design process may have been much more subtle. In fact, it may have contravened no natural laws at all. Let's consider just one possibility. Suppose the designer is indeed God, as most people would suspect. Well, then, as Kenneth Miller points out in his book *Finding Darwin's God:*

> The indeterminate nature of quantum events would allow a clever and subtle God to influence events in ways that are profound, but scientifically undetectable to us. Those events could include the appearance of mutations ... and even the survival of individual cells and organisms affected by the chance processes of radioactive decay.[12]

Miller doesn't think guidance is necessary in evolution, but if it were, as I believe, then a route would be open for a subtle God to design life without overriding natural law. If quantum events such as radioactive decay are not governed by causal laws, then it breaks no law of nature to influence such events. As a theist like Miller, I would say that seems perfectly possible. I would add, however, that such a process would amount to intelligent design, not Darwinian evolution. Further, while we might not be able to detect quantum manipulations, we may be able to conclude confidently that the final structure was designed.

Misconceptions Concerning Supposed Ways Around the Irreducibility of Biochemical Systems

Consider a hypothetical example where proteins homologous to all of the parts of an irreducibly complex molecular machine first had other individual functions in the cell. Might the irreducible system then have been put together from individual components that originally worked on their own, as some Darwinists have proposed? Unfortunately this picture greatly oversimplifies the difficulty, as I discussed in *Darwin's Black Box.*[13] Here analogies to mousetraps break down somewhat, because the parts of a molecular system have to automatically find each other in the cell. They can't be arranged by an intelligent agent, as a mousetrap is.

To find each other in the cell, interacting parts have to have their surfaces shaped so that they are very closely matched to each other, such as pictured in Figure 2. Originally, however, the individually-acting components would not have had complementary surfaces. So all of the interacting surfaces of all of the components would first have to be adjusted before they could function together. And only then would the new function of the composite system appear. Thus, I emphasize strongly, *the problem of irreducibility remains, even if individual proteins homologous to system components separately and originally had their own functions.*

Another area where one has to be careful is in noticing that some systems with extra or redundant components may have an irreducibly complex *core*. For example, a car with four spark plugs might get by with three or two, but it certainly can't get by with none. Rat traps often have two springs to give them extra strength. The trap can still work if one spring is removed, but it can't work if both springs are removed. Thus in trying to imagine the origin of a rat trap by Darwinian means, we still have all the problems we had with a mousetrap. A cellular example of redundancy is the hugely complex eukaryotic cilium, which contains about 250 distinct protein parts.[14] The cilium has multiple copies of a number of components, including multiple microtubules and dynein arms. Yet a working cilium needs at least one copy of each to work, as I pictured in my book.[15] Thus, like a rat trap, its gradual Darwinian production remains quite difficult to envision. Kenneth Miller has pointed to the redundancy of the cilium as a counterexample to my claim of its irreducibility.[16] But redundancy only delays irreducibility; it does not eliminate it.

Finally, rather than showing how their theory could handle the obstacle, some Darwinists are hoping to get around irreducible complexity by verbal tap dancing. At a debate between proponents and opponents of intelligent design sponsored by the American Museum of Natural History in April 2002, Kenneth Miller actually claimed (the transcript is available at the website of the National Center for Science Education) that a mousetrap isn't irreducibly complex because subsets of a mousetrap, and even each individual part, could still "function" on their own. The holding bar of a mousetrap, Miller observed, could be used as *a toothpick,* so it still had a "function" outside the mousetrap. Any of the parts of the trap could be used as a paperweight, he continued, so they all had "functions." And since any object that has mass

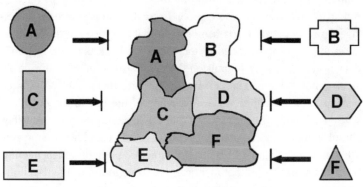

Figure 2

can be a paperweight, then any part of anything has a function of its own. *Presto,* there is no such thing as irreducible complexity! Thus the acute problem for gradualism that any child can see in systems like the mousetrap is smoothly explained away.

Of course, the facile explanation rests on a transparent fallacy, a brazen equivocation. Miller uses the word "function" in two different senses. Recall that the definition of irreducible complexity notes that removal of a part "causes the *system* to effectively cease functioning." Without saying so, in his exposition Miller shifts the focus from the separate function of the intact *system* itself to the question of whether we can find a different use (or "function") for some of the *parts*. However, if one removes a part from the mousetrap I pictured, it can no longer catch mice. The *system* has indeed effectively ceased functioning, so the *system* is irreducibly complex, just as I had written. What's more, the functions that Miller glibly assigns to the parts – paperweight, toothpick, key chain, etc. – have little or nothing to do with the function of the system of catching mice (unlike the mousetrap series proposed by John McDonald, discussed later in this chapter), so they give us no clue as to how the system's function could arise gradually. Miller explained precisely nothing.

With the problem of the mousetrap behind him, Miller moved on to the bacterial flagellum – and again resorted to the same fallacy. If nothing else, one has to admire the breathtaking audacity of verbally trying to turn another severe problem for Darwinism into an advantage. In recent years it has been shown that the bacterial flagellum is an even more sophisticated system than had been thought. Not only does it act as a rotary propulsion device, it also contains within itself an elegant mechanism to transport the proteins that make up the outer portion of the machine, from the inside of the cell to the outside.[17] Without blinking, Miller asserted that the flagellum is not irreducibly complex because some proteins of the flagellum could be missing and the remainder could still transport proteins, perhaps independently. (Proteins similar – but not identical – to some found in the flagellum occur in the type III secretory system of some bacteria.[18]) Again he was equivocating, switching the focus from the function of the system to act as a rotary propulsion machine to the ability of a subset of the system to transport proteins across a membrane. However, taking away the parts of the flagellum certainly destroys the ability of the system to act as a rotary propulsion machine, as I have argued. Thus, contra Miller, the flagellum is indeed irreducibly complex. What's more, the function of transporting proteins has as little directly to do with the function of rotary propulsion as a toothpick has to do with a mousetrap. So discovering the supportive function of transporting proteins tells us precisely nothing about how Darwinian processes might have put together a rotary propulsion machine.

The Blood Clotting Cascade

Having dealt with some common misconceptions about intelligent design, in the next several sections I will examine two systems that were proposed as serious counterexamples to my claim of irreducible complexity. I will show not only that they fail, but also how they highlight the seriousness of the obstacle of irreducible complexity.

In *Darwin's Black Box* I argued that the blood clotting cascade is an example of an irreducibly complex system.[19] As seen just by eye, clotting seems like a simple process. A small cut or scrape will bleed for a while and then slow down and stop as the visible blood congeals. However, studies over the past fifty years have shown that the visible simplicity is undergirded by a system of remarkable complexity.[20]In all there are over a score of separate protein parts involved in the vertebrate clotting system. The concerted action of the components results in formation of a weblike structure at the site of the cut, which traps red blood cells and stops bleeding. Most of the components of the clotting cascade are involved not in the structure of the clot itself but in the control of the timing and placement of the clot. After all, it would not do to have clots forming at inappropriate times and places. A clot that formed in the wrong place, such as in the heart or brain, could lead to a heart attack or stroke. Yet a clot that formed even in the right place, but too slowly, would do little good.

The insoluble weblike fibers of the clot material itself are formed of a protein called fibrin. However, an insoluble web would gum up blood flow before a cut or scrape happens, so fibrin exists in the bloodstream initially as a soluble, inactive form called fibrinogen. When the closed circulatory system is breached, fibrinogen is activated by having a piece cut off from one end of two of the three proteins which comprise it. This exposes sticky sites on the protein, which allows them to aggregate. Because of the shape of the fibrin, the molecules aggregate into long fibers that form the meshwork of the clot. Eventually, when healing is completed, the clot is removed by an enzyme called plasmin.

The enzyme which converts fibrinogen to fibrin is called thrombin. Yet the action of thrombin itself has to be carefully regulated. If it were not, then thrombin would quickly convert fibrinogen to fibrin, causing massive blood clots and rapid death. It turns out that thrombin exists in an inactive form called prothrombin, which has to be activated by another component called Stuart factor. But by the same reasoning the activity of Stuart factor has to be controlled too, and it is activated by yet another component. Ultimately the component that usually begins the cascade is tissue factor, which occurs on cells that normally do not come in contact with the circulatory system. However, when a cut occurs, blood is exposed to tissue factor, which initiates the clotting cascade.

Thus in the clotting cascade, one component acts on another, which acts on the next, and so forth. I argued that the cascade is irreducibly complex because if a component is removed the pathway is either immediately turned on or permanently turned off. It would not do, I wrote, to postulate that the pathway started from one end, fibrinogen, and added components, since fibrinogen itself does no good. Nor is it plausible to start even with something like fibrinogen and a nonspecific enzyme that might cleave it, since the clotting would not be regulated and would be much more likely to do harm than good.

So said I. But Russell Doolittle – an eminent protein biochemist, professor of biochemistry at the University of California-San Diego, member of the National Academy of Sciences, and lifelong student of the blood clotting system – disagreed. As part of a symposium discussing my book and Richard Dawkins' *Climbing Mount Improbable* in *Boston Review,* which is published by the Massachusetts Institute of Technology, Doolittle wrote an essay discussing the phenomenon of gene duplication, by which a cell may be provided with an extra copy of a functioning gene. He then conjectured that the components of the blood clotting pathway, many of which have structures similar to each other, arose by gene duplication and gradual divergence. This is the common view among Darwinists. Professor Doolittle went on to describe a then-recent experiment which, he thought, showed that the cascade is not irreducible after all. Professor Doolittle cited a paper by Bugge et al.,[21] entitled "Loss of Fibrinogen Rescues Mice from the Pleiotropic Effects of Plasminogen Deficiency." Of the paper he wrote:

> Recently the gene for plaminogen [*sic*] was knocked out of mice, and, predictably, those mice had thrombotic complications because fibrin clots could not be cleared away. Not long after that, the same workers knocked out the gene for fibrinogen in

another line of mice. Again, predictably, these mice were ailing, although in this case hemorrhage was the problem. And what do you think happened when these two lines of mice were crossed? For all practical purposes, the mice lacking both genes were normal! Contrary to claims about irreducible complexity, the entire ensemble of proteins is not needed. Music and harmony can arise from a smaller orchestra.[22]

Again, fibrinogen is the precursor of the clot material itself. Plasminogen is the precursor of plasmin, which removes clots once their purpose is accomplished. So if one knocks out either one of those genes of the clotting pathway, trouble results; but, Doolittle asserted, if one knocks out both, then the system is apparently functional again. While that would be a very interesting result, it turns out to be incorrect. Doolittle misread the paper.

The abstract of Bugge et al. (1996a) states, "Mice deficient in plasminogen and fibrinogen are phenotypically indistinguishable from fibrinogen-deficient mice." In other words, the double-mutants have all the problems that the mice lacking just plasminogen have. Those problems include inability to clot, hemorrhage, and death of females during pregnancy. Plasminogen deficiency leads to a different suite of symptoms – thrombosis, ulcers, and high mortality. Mice missing both genes were "rescued" from the ill-effects of plasminogen deficiency only to suffer the problems associated with fibrinogen deficiency.[23] The reason for this is easy to see. Plasminogen is needed to remove clots which, left in place, interfere with normal functions. However, if the gene for fibrinogen is also knocked out, then clots can't form in the first place, and their removal is not an issue. Yet if clots can't form, then there is no functioning clotting system, and the mice suffer the predictable consequences.

Clearly the double-knockout mice are not "normal." They are not promising evolutionary intermediates.

The same group which produced the mice missing plasminogen and fibrinogen have also produced mice individually missing other components of the clotting cascade – prothrombin and tissue factor. In each case the mice are severely compromised, which is *exactly* what one expects if the cascade is irreducibly complex.

What lessons can we draw from this incident? The point is certainly not that Russell Doolittle misread a paper, which anyone might do. (Scientists as a rule are not known for their ability to write clearly, and Bugge et al. were no exception.) Rather, the main lesson is that irreducible complexity seems to be a much more severe problem than Darwinists recognize, since the experiment Doolittle himself chose to demonstrate that "music and harmony can arise from a smaller orchestra" showed exactly the opposite. A second lesson is that gene duplication is not the panacea it is often made out to be. Professor Doolittle knows as much about the structures of the clotting proteins and their genes as anyone on earth, and is convinced that many of them arose by gene duplication and exon shuffling. Yet that knowledge did not prevent him from proposing utterly nonviable mutants as possible examples of evolutionary intermediates. A third lesson is that, as I had claimed in *Darwin's Black Box,* there are no papers in the scientific literature detailing how the clotting pathway could have arisen by Darwinian means. If there were, Doolittle would simply have cited them.

Another significant lesson we can draw is that, while the majority of academic biologists and philosophers place their confidence in Darwinism, that confidence rests on no firmer grounds than Professor Doolittle's. As an illustration, consider the words of the philosopher Michael Ruse:

> For example, Behe is a real scientist, but this case for the impossibility of a small-step natural origin of biological complexity has been trampled upon contemptuously by the scientists working in the field. They think his grasp of the pertinent science is weak and his knowledge of the literature curiously (although conveniently) outdated.
>
> For example, far from the evolution of clotting being a mystery, the past three decades of work by Russell Doolittle and

others has thrown significant light on the ways in which clotting came into being. More than this, it can be shown that the clotting mechanism does not have to be a one-step phenomenon with everything already in place and functioning. One step in the cascade involves fibrinogen, required for clotting, and another, plaminogen [sic], required for clearing clots away.[24]

And Ruse went on to quote Doolittle's passage from *Boston Review* that I quoted earlier. Now, Ruse is a prominent Darwinist and has written many books on various aspects of Darwiniana. Yet, as his approving quotation of Doolittle's mistaken reasoning shows (complete with copying of Doolittle's typo-misspelling of "plaminogen"), Ruse has no independent knowledge of how natural selection could have put together complex biochemical systems. As far as the scientific dispute is concerned, Ruse has nothing to add.

Another such example is seen in a recent essay in *The Scientist* entitled "Not-So-Intelligent Design," by Neil S. Greenspan, a professor of pathology at Case Western Reserve University, who wrote, "The Design advocates also ignore the accumulating examples of the reducibility of biological systems. As Russell Doolittle has noted in commenting on the writings of one ID advocate ..."[25] and Greenspan goes on to approvingly cite Doolittle's argument in *Boston Review*. He concludes with unwitting irony, "These results cast doubt on the claim by proponents of ID that they know which systems exhibit irreducible complexity and which do not." But since the results of Bugge et al. are precisely the opposite of what Greenspan supposed, the shoe is now on the other foot. This incident casts grave doubt on the claim by Darwinists, both biologists and philosophers, that they know that complex cellular systems are explainable in Darwinian terms. It demonstrates that Darwinists either cannot or will not recognize difficulties for their theory.

The Mousetrap

The second counterargument to irreducibility I will discuss here does not concern a biological example but a conceptual one. In *Darwin's*

Black Box I pointed to a common mechanical mousetrap as an example of irreducible complexity. Almost immediately after publication, some Darwinists began proposing ways that the mousetrap could be built step by step. One proposal which has gotten wide attention, and has been endorsed by some prominent scientists, was put forward by John McDonald, a professor of biology at the University of Delaware and can be seen on his website.[26] His series of traps are shown in Figure 3. McDonald's main point was that the trap I pictured in my book consisted of five parts, yet he could build a trap with fewer parts.

I agree. In fact, I said exactly the same thing in my book. I wrote:

> We need to distinguish between a *physical* precursor and a *conceptual* precursor. The trap described above is not the only system that can immobilize a mouse. On other occasions my family has used a glue trap. In theory at least, one can use a box propped open with a stick that could be tripped. Or one can simply shoot the mouse with a BB gun. However, these are not physical precursors to the standard mousetrap since they cannot be transformed, step-by-Darwinian-step, into a trap with a base, hammer, spring, catch, and holding bar.[27]

Thus the point is not that mousetraps can be built in different ways with different numbers of pieces. (My children have a game at home called Mousetrap which has many, many pieces and looks altogether different from the common mechanical one.) Of course they can. The only question is whether a particular trap can be built by "numerous, successive, slight modifications" to a simple starting point – without the intervention of intelligence – as Darwin insisted his theory required.

The McDonald traps cannot. Shown at the top of Figure 3 are his one-piece trap and his two-piece trap. The structure of the second trap, however, is not a single, small, random step away from the first. First, notice that the one-piece trap is not a simple spring – it is shaped in a very special way. In fact, the shape was deliberately chosen by an intelligent agent, John McDonald, to be able to act as a trap. Well, one has to start somewhere. But if the mousetrap series is to have any relevance at all to Darwinian evolution, then intelligence can't be involved at any further point.

Yet intelligence saturates the whole series. Consider what would be necessary to convert the one-piece trap to the "two-piece" trap. One can't just place the first trap on a simple piece of wood and have it work as the second trap does. Rather, as shown in Figure 3, the two protruding ends of the spring both first have to be reoriented. What's more, two staples (barely visible in Figure 3) are added to hold the spring onto the platform so it can be under tension in the two-piece trap. So we have gone not from a one- to a two-piece trap, but from a one- to a four-piece trap. Notice also that the placement of the staples in relation to the edge of the platform is critical. If the staples were moved a quarter inch from where they are, the trap wouldn't work. Finally, consider that to have a serious analogy to the robotic processes of the cell we can't have an intelligent human setting the mousetrap – the first trap would have to be set by some unconscious charging mechanism. So, when the pieces are rearranged, the charging mechanism too would have to change for the second trap.

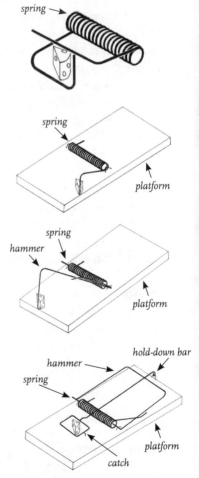

It's easy for us intelligent agents to overlook our role in directing the construction of a system, but nature cannot overlook any step at all, so

Figure 3

the McDonald mousetrap series completely fails as an analogy to Darwinian evolution. In fact, the second trap is best viewed not as some Darwinian descendant of the first, but as a completely different trap, designed by an intelligent agent, perhaps using a refashioned part or two from the first trap.

Each of the subsequent steps of the series suffers from analogous problems, which I have discussed elsewhere.[28]

In his endorsement of the McDonald mousetrap series, Kenneth Miller wrote: "If simpler versions of this mechanical device [the mousetrap] can be shown to work, then simpler versions of biochemical machines could work as well … and this means that complex biochemical machines could indeed have had functional precursors." But that is exactly what it doesn't show – if by "precursor" Miller means "Darwinian precursor." On the contrary, McDonald's mousetrap series shows that even if one does find a simpler system to perform some function, that gives us no reason to think a more complex system performing the same function could be produced by a Darwinian process starting with the simpler system. Rather, the difficulty in doing so for a simple mousetrap gives us compelling reason to think it cannot be done for complex molecular machines.

Future Prospects of the Intelligent Design Hypothesis

The misconceived arguments by Darwinists that I have recounted here strongly encourage me that the hypothesis of intelligent design is on the right track. After all, if well-informed opponents of an idea attack it by citing data that, when considered objectively, actually show its force, then one is entitled to be confident that the idea is worth investigating.

Yet it is not primarily the inadequacy of Darwinist responses that bodes well for the design hypothesis. Rather, the strength of design derives mainly from the work-a-day progress of science. To appreciate this fact, it is important to realize that the idea of intelligent design arose not from the work of any individual but from the collective work of biology, particularly in the last fifty years. Fifty years ago the cell seemed much simpler, and in our innocence it was easier then to think that Darwinian processes might have accounted for it. But as biology progressed and the imagined simplicity vanished, the idea of design became more and more compelling. That trend is continuing inexorably. The cell is not getting any simpler; it is getting much more complex. I will conclude this chapter by citing just one example, from the relatively new area of proteomics.

With the successful sequencing of the entire genomes of dozens of microorganisms and one vertebrate (us), the impetus has turned toward analyzing the cellular interactions of the proteins that the genomes code for, taken as a whole. Remarkable progress has already been made. Early in 2002 an exhaustive study was reported of the proteins comprising the yeast proteome.[29] Among other questions, the investigators asked what proportion of yeast proteins worked as groups. They discovered that nearly fifty percent of proteins work as complexes of a half dozen or more, and many as complexes of ten or more.[30]

This is not at all what Darwinists expected. As Bruce Alberts wrote earlier in the article "The Cell as a Collection of Protein Machines":

We have always underestimated cells. Undoubtedly we still do today. But at least we are no longer as naive as we were when I was a graduate student in the 1960s. Then most of us viewed cells as containing a giant set of second-order reactions....

But, as it turns out, we can walk and we can talk because the chemistry that makes life possible is much more elaborate and sophisticated than anything we students had ever considered. Proteins make up most of the dry mass of a cell. But instead of a cell dominated by randomly colliding individual protein molecules, we now know that nearly every major process in a cell is carried out by assemblies of 10 or more protein molecules. And, as it carries out its biological functions, each of these protein assemblies interacts with several other large complexes of proteins. Indeed, the entire cell can be viewed as a factory that contains an elaborate network of interlocking assembly lines, each of which is composed of a set of large protein machines.[31]

The important point here for a theory of intelligent design is that molecular machines are not confined to the few examples I discussed in *Darwin's Black Box*. Rather, most proteins are found as components of complicated molecular machines. Thus design might extend to a large fraction of the features of the cell, and perhaps beyond that into higher levels of biology.

Progress in twentieth-century science has led us to the design hypothesis. I expect progress in the twenty-first century to confirm and extend it.

CHAPTER 7

The Origin of Life

Srila Prabhupada: If life originated from chemicals, and if your science is so advanced, then why can't you create life biochemically in your laboratories?

Karandhara: They say they will create life in the future.

Srila Prabhupada: What future? When this crucial point is raised they reply, "We shall do it in the future." Why in the future? ... If they are so advanced, they must demonstrate now how life can be created from chemicals.... They are talking nonsense.

Karandhara: They say that they are right on the verge of creating life.

Srila Prabhupada: That's only a different way of saying the same thing: "In the future." The scientists must admit that they still do not know the origin of life.... Their claim that they will soon prove a chemical origin of life is something like paying someone with a postdated check. What is the value of that check? Scientists are claiming that their science is wonderful, but when a practical example is wanted they say they will provide it in the future ... The scientists cannot produce even a single blade of grass in their laboratories, yet they are claiming that life is produced from chemicals. What is this nonsense? Is no one questioning this? (From a conversation held on April 19, 1973, in Los Angeles, USA)

* * *

Darwin did not discuss the origin of life in *On the Origin of Species*. Rather, his theory started from the assumption that life already existed, if only in the form of one or more self-replicating organisms. From there, he theorized, millions of species were generated. But although he did not discuss life's origin, he did make certain crucial assumptions that are worth recognizing – for example, that the first forms of life were ultimately simple. That is, that the gap between noncomplex, nonliving chemicals and living organisms was small. To Darwin and other scientists of his time, this was a logical assumption. After all, nineteenth-century microscopes were not particularly powerful, and through them the cell appeared to be an uncomplicated bag of mixed, disorganized chemicals. It seemed reasonable that life could have arisen all at once from a chance combination of these chemicals. In 1863 Darwin wrote a letter to botanist Joseph Hooker in which he expressed this: "But if (and oh! what a big if!) we could conceive in some warm little pond, with all sorts of ammonia and phosphoric salts, light, heat, electricity, etc., present, that a protein compound was chemically formed ready to undergo still more complex changes ..."[1]

Nevertheless, to his credit Darwin understood that it was beyond the science of his time to say much about how life had originated. Further to Hooker: "It is mere rubbish thinking at present of the origin of life; one might as well think of the origin of matter."

Despite Darwin's warning about speculating on the origin of life, the idea of the spontaneous chemical generation of life was widely accepted in Darwin's time, and Darwin himself was inclined toward it. There is an incident that illustrates how much scientists believed it. Around 1857 Thomas Huxley came across some peculiar-looking mud pulled up from the bottom of the North Sea. For a number of years he and other scientists thought it a sample of *Urschleim* (primordial slime), the chemical origin of life. Philip Rehbock writes:

At the meeting of the British Association for the Advancement of Science in August 1868, Thomas Huxley announced the results of his microscopial examination of some specimens of North Atlantic bottom sediment. Among the constituents of these seemingly unexciting specimens Huxley had found some curious "granule-heaps" surrounded by extensive masses of viscous matter, which he described variously as "lumps of a transparent, gelatinous substance" and a "colorless and structureless matrix." Tests of the substance convinced Huxley that he was dealing with a new type of organism in the form of virtually undifferentiated protoplasm. He gave the organism the generic name *Bathybius,* after its oceanic habitat, and called the species *B. haeckelii,* after his friend and fellow champion of Darwinism Ernst Haeckel.

Bathybius haeckelii was to live a brief but eventful life of some seven years. In 1875 the scientists aboard HMS *Challenger,* then nearing the end of their epochal voyage for the establishment of the new science of oceanography, discovered that *Bathybius* was nothing more than an inorganic precipitate. Despite his obvious embarrassment, Huxley readily admitted his error. Haeckel, however, who had applauded Huxley's original discovery, would not give up so easily. For him *Bathybius* was both an important member of his new class of unicellular organisms, the Monera, and a keystone in his mechanistic philosophy of life.[2]

In the decades following Darwin it became clear that the cell was more complicated than anyone had previously thought, and spontaneous generation of a cell from simple chemicals began to seem unlikely. At the beginning of the twentieth century scientists such as the Russian chemist Alexander Oparin (1894–1980) began to take a different approach to the question of how life had originated. Oparin outlined an elaborate set of chemical changes that could lead to the formation of the first cell. The process, he said, would take a long time – hundreds of millions, perhaps billions, of years. He proposed that ammonia (NH_3), methane (CH_4), hydrogen (H_2), carbon dioxide (CO_2), and water vapor (H_2O), with ultraviolet light as an energy source, would combine with the metallic elements dissolved in water. This would produce a nitrogen-rich prebiotic soup in which simple hydrocarbon molecules would form. These would combine into amino acids, sugars, and phosphates, which in turn would form proteins. The molecule groups reacting together in this way would become attracted to one another and surround themselves with chemical walls of some type, resulting in the precursors to the first cells. Oparin called them "coacervates." These primitive cells would then compete for survival, becoming more complex and therefore more stable.

Oparin's ideas remained largely untested until 1953, when Stanley Miller, a graduate student at the University of Chicago, performed the now-famous experiment seen at the time to be a confirmation of Oparin's hypothesis. In the laboratory Miller sent electric sparks through a combination of methane, ammonia, hydrogen, and water vapor. A week later he analyzed the results and found traces of several amino acids. Worldwide headlines announced Miller's experiment: scientists were now creating the building blocks of life! According to *Time* magazine: "Graduate Student Stanley L. Miller, 23, told how he had simulated conditions on a primitive earth and created out of its atmospheric gases several organic compounds that are close to proteins."[3]

Of course, *Time* magazine didn't mention that the difference between an amino acid and a protein is something like the difference between a brick and a building. Nevertheless, the research into life's origins had never before (and has never since) experienced such a boost of enthusiastic interest as Miller's experiment generated. A number of scientists were convinced that they were about to discover life's secrets. Research increased manifold as universities and research institutions around the world joined the hunt for the chemical pathway they believed life had taken.

Now, however, more than fifty years later, experts in the field readily admit that their successes have not been commensurate with their efforts. Thus in 2003 Simon Conway Morris began a chapter on the origin-of-life research in his book *Life's Solution* with the sentence "This chapter is a story of abject scientific failure."[4]

What has happened instead from the time of Miller's experiment is that biochemists have uncovered a marvel of complexity inside the cell. This biochemical revolution (which is the only apt word here) was initiated by another remarkable feat: the discovery of the double helix structure of DNA, announced in April 1953, just four weeks before Miller went public with his experiment, by Francis Crick and James Watson, who shared a Nobel Prize for their achievement.

Unfortunately, scientists still cannot state unequivocally how life originated.

In the years that followed, more discoveries were made – how proteins are synthesized, the genetic code, and the role of RNA, to name a few. Today it is known that the complexity of the cell's nanotechnology far surpasses anything else found in nature – or in the man-made world, for that matter. We now know that the cell is like a huge factory with production machines lined up as far as the eye can see, manufacturing millions of commodities, mainly in the shape of thousands of complex proteins. Each second, the cell produces about 1,000 new proteins, proteins that in many cases are themselves ingenious nanomachines or parts of other nanomachines, each of which performs one or more functions in the organism.

Where do these discoveries leave origin-of-life research? Although scientists working in the field are still hopeful that life can be reduced to chemistry and that it is feasible to uncover life's chemical secrets, there is no longer consensus on what questions should be asked. There are theories, though, and their proponents can point out with precision the defects in opposing theories. Unfortunately, scientists still cannot state unequivocally how life originated.

We will now discuss some of the difficulties in the different origin-of-life theories.[5]

Was the Atmosphere Reducing?

In experiments like Stanley Miller's, scientists have tried to simulate conditions as they assume they were on the early earth. Miller and most of those who have followed him have, for example, assumed that the early earth had a "reducing atmosphere" – that is, an atmosphere devoid of free oxygen (O_2). This seems to be a necessary condition for life to appear because oxygen effectively hinders the formation of organic compounds like amino acids; should they form despite the free oxygen in the environment, the free oxygen would quickly destroy them. Free oxygen, then, must have been produced only later, after plants had evolved and begun to use photosynthesis.

But as it turns out this assumption is most likely false. Today both geologists and geoscientists agree that the earth's early atmosphere did in fact contain a significant amount of free oxygen.[6] Although this means that the free oxygen could not have come from photosynthesis, other processes also create oxygen – photodissociation, for example, in which ultraviolet rays from the sun split water molecules into their components, hydrogen and oxygen. The hydrogen would have left the earth's atmosphere because of its lightness, and the oxygen, being heavier, would have remained. Quite a few minerals react with oxygen in a process called oxidization. That there must have been oxygen in the early atmosphere has been confirmed by scientists discovering traces of oxidization in rocks from the oldest known strata, from before life on earth is supposed to have begun.[7]

The presence of free oxygen would have effectively prevented the formation of ammonia and methane, two main ingredients in Miller's hypothetical early earth atmosphere. It follows, therefore, that the Miller experiment was not based on a realistic simulation of the earth's atmosphere, which renders his experiment invalid.

Also flawed in his experiment was his assumption that the early atmosphere had ample hydrogen. Scientists have now concluded that whatever free hydrogen there was quickly escaped the earth's atmosphere and floated into outer space.[8] With no hydrogen to react with the carbon dioxide and nitrogen, methane and ammonia could not have formed, again nullifying Miller's experiment.

Subsequent experiments that allowed for these factors did not result in the production of any amino acids, or at best produced only the simplest amino acid, glycine. This leaves the other nineteen amino acids unaccounted for.

Chemical Evolution Running Backwards

Experiments like Miller's run up against the difficulty of explaining how chemical compounds, once formed, were not immediately destroyed. In his experiment Miller removed the chemical compounds from the spark discharges as soon as they were formed in order to protect them for later analysis. No one is moving such compounds in nature; the same energy source that would have created the compounds would most likely have also quickly destroyed them.

Interferring Cross-reactions

Miller's experiment did produce amino acids, but it also produced a host of other compounds. Most of these were irrelevant to and in many cases poisonous to life as we know it. What could have kept the amino acids on the early earth from reacting with these toxic compounds? Again, this problem is easily solved in a laboratory: one simply has to isolate the amino acids. But a laboratory is not a realistic simulation of nature.

Inside a cell, amino acids bind with other amino acids and with the help of enzymes form proteins. Without the enzymes as catalysts, however, amino acids do not readily link with one another but tend to react instead with other substances, such as sugars. The implication of this, of course, is that in a setting where amino acids are free to choose, so to speak, they will generally combine in all sorts of cross-reactions with components other than other amino acids and thus be unavailable for anything biologically useful. This is why Stanley Miller's experiments and experiments of a similar type have produced predominantly large amounts of nonbiological sludge (mainly "tars"). Miller's mentor, Harold Urey, called this sludge *"beilstein,"* a word that refers to a comprehensive database of all known organic compounds. In fact, one would expect experiments like Miller's to produce a small amount of amino acids, since such experiments are bound to create an array of simple organic compounds.

For there to be truth to the story of the chemical origin of life that Oparin proposed and Miller tried to verify, there would need to have been a concentrated form of simple biological compounds (a "prebiotic soup") before they could have combined to form the complex biological macromolecules necessary for life. But there is no evidence that nature can concentrate simple chemical compounds and later have them arrange themselves into those large complex molecules. Neither have geologists ever found anything that would indicate that such concentration and rearrangement of molecules and macromolecules ever occurred. There are numerous clay deposits in the world that would have preserved evidence of a prebiotic soup, but no such evidence exists. In *The Mystery of Life's Origin,* Thaxton, Bradley, and Olsen write,

> [If there ever was a prebiotic soup] ... The earliest Precambrian deposits would be expected to contain unusually large proportions of hydrocarbon material or its carbon remains. They do not, however.[9]

Brooks and Shaw similarly write in *Origin and Development of Living Systems,*

> If there ever was a primitive soup, then we would expect to find at least somewhere on this planet either massive sediments containing enormous amounts of the various nitrogenous organic

THE ORIGIN OF LIFE 113

compounds, amino acids, purines, pyrimidines, and the like, or alternatively in much metamorphosed sediments we should find vast amounts of nitrogenous cokes. In fact no such materials have been found anywhere on earth.[10]

Give Me the Right Hand

Amino acids come in two varieties, "left-handed" acids and "right-handed" acids. Think of a pair of gloves. The right-hand glove and the left-hand glove are identical except that they are mirror images of one another. Similarly, left-handed and right-handed amino acids share the same chemical formula and structure but are mirror images. When amino acids are formed either in experiments or in nature (except within living cells), an equal amount of left- and right-handed acids results. However, when proteins are formed in living cells, with rare exceptions only left-handed amino acids occur.

No one knows why amino acids occur in only one of the two possible forms in living organisms. If life is the result of an unguided chemical process, there must exist a chemical process that selects one form of the amino acid and completely excludes the other. To date, no such process has been found.

This is also true of the sugars that form the backbone of DNA and RNA. Although an equal amount of right-handed and left-handed sugars form both in the laboratory and in nature (outside living cells), cells use only right-handed sugars when building DNA and RNA.

Creating the Polymers

Proteins, DNA, and RNA all consist of long molecular chains known as polymers. What biological function polymers execute depends on the precise sequence of the individual units (monomers) in the chain. Proteins, which consist of chains of amino acids, are on average hundreds of amino acids long, whereas DNA can consist of millions of nucleotide bases. Were we to try to create the building blocks of life in a laboratory, and even if we assume we could create a large amount of the correct sugars (right-handed, or D-sugars) and the correct kind of amino acids (left-handed, or L-amino acids), the real construction work would still remain. L-amino acids need to be combined in the correct sequence to form proteins, and nucleotide bases need to be attached to a D-sugar-phosphate backbone to form DNA and RNA.

In the proteins made in living cells, amino acids are connected only by peptide bonds. Amino acids can react and bind in several ways, but living organisms use only one way. No one knows why. Furthermore, the bonding of the proteins has to be linear; although proteins have the potential to side-branch – something common in nonbiological organic compounds – they do not do so. And amino acids have to be arranged in a specific order. There are twenty amino acids that combine in innumerable ways. However, for their combination to make a functional protein, they must assemble according to a certain order, just as letters have to be arranged in a particular sequence to make meaningful words.

The origin of life has turned out to be much more difficult than most people envisioned.

The same constraints apply to the nucleotide sequences in DNA. Only one kind of bond, the 3'–5' phosphodiester linkage, is biologically relevant, although other bonds in nonbiological contexts are equally possible.

Cells use only the correct bonds, and order singular units in the correct order through the action of enzymes and the ribosomes. However, enzymes and ribosomes presuppose the entire DNA-RNA-protein machinery. Since it is precisely this fact that origin-of-life research is trying to explain, it follows that this very machinery cannot be a part of the explanation of how it came about in the first place. Almost no origin-of-life researchers have even attempted to explain how this chicken-and-egg arrangement got there.

These examples give just a hint of the ever-mounting problems that face origin-of-life research. Stanley Miller was already admitting problems by 1991: "The origin of life has turned out to be much more difficult than I, and most other people, envisioned."[11]

The RNA World

Those familiar with popular science literature may have come across the phrase "the RNA world," coined in the 1980s by Dr. Walter Gilbert, who proposed that the first pre-life molecules were not proteins or DNA but RNA. RNA can, like DNA, store information, but it can also catalyze reactions the way proteins do. Gilbert hypothesized that RNA may have therefore supported the development of cellular life and evolved into the DNA and protein world of today. DNA, through its greater chemical stability, took over the role of data storage, whereas protein, which is more flexible in catalysis due to the large variety of amino acids, became the specialized catalytic molecules.

In cells, RNA forms the link between DNA and proteins. During protein synthesis RNA copies the relevant section of DNA – a gene – and carries the copied gene out from the cell's nucleus to the ribosomes, where the message delivered by RNA is translated into long chains of amino acids. These amino acids are then folded into specific proteins.

Thus RNA has features of both DNA and protein. Like DNA, RNA is a vehicle for genetic information, and like proteins it is involved in catalysis. It seemed feasible for Gilbert and others to theorize, therefore, that RNA may have been the first polymer to spontaneously appear on earth. DNA and protein would then have been later developments.

Many have gotten the impression that "the RNA world" answers the challenges facing experiments like Miller's, all of which assume that protein was the first to appear. However, and without getting into the technical details, it has been found that "the RNA world" faces exactly the same problems of the proteins-first theory faces. If there had indeed been an "RNA world" at life's beginnings, RNA could have developed only from its later subunits, and how these subunits could have formed on the early earth is as unsolved as the question of where the molecules to form proteins could have come from.

Today, leading origin-of-life researchers do not consider RNA a likely candidate for the first biologically relevant compound to have spontaneously arisen. These researchers include Leslie Orgel and Gerald Joyce, probably the most cited origin-of-life researchers within the last decades. Gerald Joyce wrote in 2002: "If the building blocks of RNA were available in the prebiotic environment, if these combined to form polynucleotides, and if some of the polynucleotides began to self-replicate, then the RNA world may have emerged as the first form of life on earth. But based on current knowledge of prebiotic chemistry, this is unlikely to have been the case."[12]

Joyce's comment underscores what he and Orgel wrote in 1999: "Thus the evidence indicates that the presence of even short nucleic acids four billion years ago would have been a near miracle."[13] Nucleic acids are the building blocks of RNA.

Robert Shapiro, professor of chemistry at the University of New York, echoed the same conclusion in 2007: "No physical law need be broken for spontaneous RNA formation to happen, but the chances against it are so immense that the suggestion implies that the nonliving world had an innate desire to generate RNA. The majority of origin-of-life scientists who still support the RNA-first theory either accept this concept (implicitly, if not explicitly) or feel that the immensely unfavorable odds were simply overcome by good luck."[14]

If Pigs Could Fly: Metabolism First

The research into the origin of life separated into two disparate approaches in the 1990s. One, "the genetic party," assumes that life started with the formation of one of the genetic macromolecules – protein, DNA, or RNA – that conduct the processes in life as we know it. The other school, "the metabolic party," proposes that life started with small molecules, first establishing the metabolism systems of life; the genetic macromolecules, they say, came later.

The metabolism-first school proposes that life arose as a catalyzed chemical cycle in a protected environment spurred on by a constant flow of energy – perhaps near a volcano. The theory proposes that a number of chemical compounds (let's call them A, B, C, and D) established a catalytic cycle. This means that A catalyzes B (in the presence of A, more B is generated). B in turn catalyzes C and C catalyzes D. If D, then, is a catalyst for A, with a constant energy flow a metabolic cycle will become established, and the amount of each compound will increase at a constant rate. Given enough time, the cycle will increase in complexity and will eventually become life as we know it.

Although this is considered the most likely scenario by researchers like Robert Shapiro, Leslie Orgel wrote a devastating critique of the theory in his last paper, published posthumously in January 2008 (Dr. Orgel died in October 2007). Among other objections, he pointed out the complete lack of evidence for the theory. In his conclusion he wrote,

> Almost all proposals of hypothetical metabolic cycles have recognized that each of the steps involved must occur rapidly enough for the cycle to be useful in the time available for its operation. It is always assumed that this condition is met, but in no case have persuasive supporting arguments been presented. Why should one believe that an ensemble of minerals that are capable of catalyzing each of the many steps of the reverse citric acid cycle was present anywhere on the primitive Earth, or that the cycle mysteriously organized itself topographically on a metal sulfide surface? The lack of a supporting background in chemistry is even more evident in proposals that metabolic cycles can evolve to "lifelike" complexity. The most serious challenge to proponents of metabolic cycle theories – the problems presented by the lack of specificity of most nonenzymatic catalysts – has, in general, not been appreciated. If it has, it has been ignored. Theories of the origin of life based on metabolic cycles cannot be justified by the inadequacy of competing theories: they must stand on their own.[15]

Dr. Orgel's final words were sarcastic: "However, solutions offered by supporters of geneticist or metabolist scenarios that are dependent on 'if pigs could fly' hypothetical chemistry are unlikely to help."[16]

Robert Shapiro and Leslie Orgel are two eminent researchers in the field of origin-of-life, representing two different views. But one thing that stands out here is that although neither of them may admit it, their severe critiques effectively dismantle both positions.

The Information Challenge

Although life's origins remain a mystery, scientists in the field still more or less universally embrace the idea that life can be reduced to chemistry. George M. Whitesides stated in 2007: "Most chemists believe, as do I, that life emerged spontaneously from mixtures of molecules in the prebiotic earth. How? I have no idea. I *believe* that understanding the cell is ultimately a question of chemistry and chemists are, in principle, best qualified to solve it."[17] (emphasis in the original)

Is Whitesides's assumption justified? One might argue that certain features, such as the information processing that goes on inside a cell, cannot be the result of chemical processes but necessarily must be intelligently designed.

Everyone understands that the cell processes information much like a computer. Even IT guru Bill Gates once stated, "Human DNA is like a computer program, but far, far more advanced than any software we've ever created."[18] The hint that more than chemistry is involved in the origin of DNA caused chemist and philosopher of science Michael Polanyi to state, "A book or any other object bearing a pattern that communicates information is essentially irreducible to physics and chemistry ... We must refuse to regard the pattern by which the DNA spreads information as part of its chemical properties."[19] Without explicitly stating it, Polanyi hinted that an underlying intelligence must be at work.

According to Polanyi the information DNA contains can no more be reduced to chemistry than the ideas in a book can be reduced to paper and ink. Even if one were to analyze to the minutest degree the chemical properties of the paper and ink a book like the one you're holding is made of, one would still not find the slightest clue about the message the book contains. The message is something different from the paper and ink; it has a completely different origin than the media used to convey it. The message could be conveyed on a thousand different media without the meanings being affected in any way.

Just as a book consists of paper and ink *and* a message independently inscribed into the paper with the ink, a computer consists of hardware and software. The hardware is the tangible matter and machinery of the computer, and the software is the information inscribed into the computer's memory. Software is not dependent on hardware; it is independently written onto the hardware in the same way that a book's message is written onto paper with ink.

Similarly, DNA also has hardware and software. The sugar and phosphate molecules, along with the four nucleotides (adenine, cytosine, guanine, and thymine) – the chemicals that make up DNA – are DNA's hardware, and the particular sequence in which the DNA's nucleotides are arranged is the software.

Computer software is written in binary code and consists of a long series of ones and zeros. With DNA the code is not binary – using only two numerals – but quaternary, using the four nucleotide letters A, C, G, and T. The sequence of the nucleotides along the DNA string codes all the information a cell needs to perform one or more of the thousands of functions in a living organism.

The genetic code was uncovered in the early 1960s, and first discovered was how it arranges for the synthesizing of proteins. Proteins are made up of chains of twenty amino acids, and particular proteins are coded for in the DNA. A triplet of three letters of the DNA alphabet codes for each amino acid. For example, the amino acid threonine is called ACU in DNA speak, and GGT codes for glycine. However, there is nothing in the chemical properties of a nucleotide that determines this coding system. For all we know, any other combination could have worked as well.

The genetic code is thus similar to any other code whether found in a language, in software, or in Morse code. In this context we can ask how such a code came to be in the first place. Nothing chemically specifies the code, and this speaks against the idea that the code has a chemical origin. All the codes whose origins we know have an intelligent origin. An obvious suggestion, therefore, is that the genetic code could also have an intelligent origin.

This inference has clear implications for the question of how life originated. Are today's scientists engaged in an undertaking that in the future will be seen as a sheer impossibility, since in the future we will understand that life does not have chemical origins? Will future generations of scientists one day look on today's origin-of-life researchers in the way today's scientists view medieval alchemists?

CHAPTER 8

The Molecular Evidence

For the first hundred years after Darwin published *Origin*, proponents of his theory sought to support it in two ways: by comparing fossils with similar anatomical features, and by comparing the embryos of one animal with another. However, as the 1950s dawned, advances in biochemistry revolutionized evolutionary theory. Scientists could suddenly see things in much more detail on the molecular level. Molecular evidence, therefore – especially evidence gathered by comparing molecular sequences from one organism to another – began to play a role in the attempt to support evolution.

Better biochemistry and more advanced equipment allowed biologists to look more closely at the components of the cell. Certain proteins, RNA molecules, and genes are common to all (or at least many) species, but the precise sequence of the amino acids in the proteins and the nucleotides in both the RNA and DNA differ from species to species. Scientists assume that these differences are caused by evolution. Therefore, comparing these sequences has become a major way to try to establish evolutionary relationships between various organisms.

Today, proponents of evolution claim, as expressed in a publication from the U.S. National Academy of Sciences in 2008, that molecular analysis "has fully confirmed the general conclusions drawn from the fossil record, the geographic distribution of species, and other types of observations."[1] However, on closer inspection we find that much of the molecular evidence actually challenges the overall conception of evolution. In many cases molecular analyses have either failed to establish relationships between species or have indicated relationships quite different from those established by anatomical comparison and fossil studies. Not only that, but molecular studies undertaken in different labs often give inconsistent results, and broad molecular comparisons made across the living kingdom reveal no evolutionary relationships at all.

Equidistance

When it became possible, for example, to chart the sequence of the amino acids in the hemoglobin of various organisms, it was found that the sequences differed noticeably. This made it possible to classify organisms according to their molecular differences. This system was seen as a powerful classification tool because it allowed biologists to mathematically quantify differences between species – something that had not previously been possible (how can differences in anatomical shapes be mathematically quantified?). Now, if an amino acid sequence of 100 units was found to differ in twenty places when two species were compared, it could be said that there was a 20 percent difference between the two species.

By and large, the results of the molecular classification matched those of the traditional classifications already established by fossils and comparative anatomy, dividing organisms into plants and animals, which are then further divided into arthropods, vertebrates, fish, amphibians, reptiles, mammals, birds, etc. What the molecules *didn't* reveal were clear evolutionary relationships between these classifications. We can see this when we examine the comparison of the cytochrome C protein, which is found in most organisms.

Using cytochrome C to compare, it turns out that the molecular difference – and therefore the evolutionary distance – between, say, a bacterium and almost any other class of life – insects, fish, plants, amphibians, reptiles, or mammals, for example – is about the same. An evolutionist would naturally expect that fish and amphibians would be closer to one another than either group is to bacteria, and amphibians would be closer to fish than they are to reptiles. But it turns out that all of them are a distance of between 64 to 69 percent away from bacteria. The same proves true when we compare insects to all the vertebrate orders (fish, amphibians, reptiles, birds, and mammals): all vertebrate orders are equidistant from insects by 25 to 30 percent. And the same holds true within the vertebrate phylum. Amphibians should have been evolutionarily closer to fish than reptiles are, and reptiles should be closer to fish than mammals and birds are. But this is not the case. Mammals, birds, reptiles, and amphibians are all equidistant from fish by 13 to 14 percent. The same pattern holds true down to the levels of genera and species, where it becomes impossible through molecular analysis to establish which species are evolutionary intermediates of what. Rather, the phenomenon of "equidistance" is pervasive in the living world.[2]

The Failure to Establish Phylogenies

Overall, it has not been possible to establish clear evolutionary relationships between organisms through molecular analysis.[3] Different studies have reached widely different conclusions. Vertebrates have generally been classified as closer to arthropods (insects and crustaceans) than to nematodes (a group of roundworms). However, in 1997 Anna Marie Aguinaldo placed insects and nematodes at an equal distance from mammals on the basis of molecular studies.[4] Biologist Michael Lynch contested this finding in 1999 when he pointed out that different results could be achieved based on the method used or even on which laboratory performed the analysis when the method was the same. Lynch writes, "Clarification of the phylogenetic relationships of the major animal phyla has been an elusive problem, with analyses based on different genes and even different analyses based on the same genes yielding a diversity of phylogenetic trees."[5]

Lynch was hoping that improved methods would make clear how

different animal phyla relate to one another. But the controversies have persisted. In 2000, French molecular biologist André Adoutte presented a new animal phylogeny derived from new rRNA-based comparisons.[6] Then, in 2002, after comparing over one hundred proteins, American biologist Jaime E. Blair concluded: "The grouping of nematodes with arthropods is an artifact that arose from the analysis of a single gene, 18s rRNA. The results presented here suggest caution in revising animal phylogeny from analyses of one or a few genes... Our results indicate that insects (arthropods) are genetically evolutionarily closer to humans (vertebrates) than to nematodes."[7]

In 2004, Yuri I. Wolf placed humans closer to flies than to nematodes after analyzing over five hundred proteins with three different phylogenetic methods.[8] The next year, after having analyzed 146 genes and thirty-five species in twelve animal phyla, the French biologist Hervé Philippe concluded that arthropods are related to nematodes and neither is closer than the other to vertebrates.[9] This didn't solve the conflict. In a comment on Philippe's work, Martin Jones and Mark Blaxter, both evolutionary biologists from the University of Edinburgh, wrote, "Despite the comforting certainty of textbooks and 150 years of argument, the true relationships of the major groups (phyla) of animals remain contentious."[10] They predicted that the molecular tree of life would "sprout new shoots – and new controversies – very soon." Not long afterwards, in December of 2005, biologist Antonis Rokas and his colleagues used two methods to analyze fifty genes from seventeen animal groups. They concluded that "different phylogenetic analyses can reach contradictory inferences with absolute support" and that the evolutionary relationships among the phyla "remain unresolved."[11]

Universal Common Descent

According to Darwinism all living organisms share a common ancestor. In the 1980s American microbiologist Carl Woese headed a project to chart the tree of life and identify "the universal common ancestor" through molecular analysis. However, by the end of the century, things were more unclear than ever. Molecular biologists James A. Lake et al.

stated, "When scientists started analyzing a variety of genes from different organisms, they ... found that their relationships to each other contradicted the evolutionary tree of life derived from rRNA alone."[12] This was confirmed by Hervé Philippe and Patrick Forterre: "With more and more sequences available, it turned out that most protein phylogenies contradict each other as well as the rRNA tree."[13]

Woese wrote in 1998, "No consistent organismal phylogeny has emerged from the many individual protein phylogenies so far produced."[14] He concluded that this was because unicellular organisms had acquired many of their genes and proteins not through gradual evolution but through "lateral gene transfer," in which one organism directly exchanges genes with another. "The universal ancestor," wrote Woese, "is not an entity, a thing, but a community of complex molecules – a sort of primordial soup – from which different kinds of cells emerged independently."

To date, the controversy over the universal tree of life has not been settled.

Around the time Woese made this statement evolutionary biologist W. Ford Doolittle echoed it. Doolittle proposed that it might be impossible to ever discover the true tree of life because there never was such a tree: "[T]he history of life cannot properly be represented as a tree."[15] Others proposed that such a tree of life did indeed exist and that it had a real root (a common ancestor) but that the root was not a simple cell without a nucleus, as is commonly thought, but a complex cell with a nucleus from which more simple cells had devolved.[16] Of course, this doesn't explain where the complex cell came from in the first place.

To date, the controversy over the universal tree of life has not been settled. Woese continues to suggest that scientists must give up Darwin's idea of common descent – "The root of the universal tree is an artifact resulting from forcing the evolutionary course into a tree representation when that representation is inappropriate"[17] – whereas others cling to the idea of a common ancestor.

Whether either view is correct remains to be seen, but it is certain that molecular biology has so far failed to establish universal common ancestry and the true phylogenies of all species. Apparently, when official scientific bodies such as the U.S. National Academy of Sciences issue statements like "The molecular evidence has fully confirmed the general conclusions drawn from the fossil record, the geographic distribution of species, and other types of observations,"[18] they should be taken with a grain of salt.

Mitochondrial Eve

When trying to trace out human history, until late in the twentieth century evolutionists had to content themselves with studies of fossils and other artifacts. With the development of molecular biology, however, it appeared possible to map human lineages simply by comparing molecular sequences.

Since the 1980s some scientists have now been claiming that on the basis of such molecular evidence they can trace the common ancestor of all humans back to a woman who lived in Africa about 200,000 years ago. This has come to be known as the African Eve theory or the Out-of-Africa theory.[19]

The African Eve theory is based on studies of mitochondrial DNA in females. Most DNA in humans is found in the nucleus of the cell, but cells also contain small round compartments called mitochondria, which exist outside the nucleus and also hold a small amount of DNA.

The DNA in a cell's nucleus is a mixture of DNA from both parents, and is organized in chromosomes, of which all human cells have forty-six. Of course, gametes (egg and sperm cells) have half that number at twenty-three chromosomes each. When an egg cell and a sperm cell combine, the cells of the resultant offspring again have forty-six chromosomes in their nuclei, twenty-three from each parent. In this way the nuclear DNA is a combination of DNA from both the mother and the father.

However, mitochondrial DNA comes only from the mother.[20] In an offspring's first cell, all the cell's machinery, including the mitochondria, is found in the egg cell of the mother – the sperm cell contributes only its twenty-three chromosomes to the nucleus. All of us therefore have mitochondrial DNA coming only from our mother, who received it only from her mother. Thus except for random mutations, this DNA has been passed down unchanged from mother to daughter since the first human mother, dubbed "Mitochondrial Eve."

The African Eve researchers claim that Mitochondrial Eve lived in Africa about 200,000 years ago. They reached this conclusion by taking the mutation rate of mitochondrial DNA and comparing it with differences in the mitochondrial DNA in various human populations around the world. In this way, they believe they can sort out which population has parented a particular other population and how long ago the two populations split.

What this means in practice is that genetic researchers have run large numbers of mitochondrial DNA sequences from groups of people all over the world through computer programs that sort the data into statistical trees. They then try to assess which statistical tree appears to require the least number of evolutionary changes to explain its data. This tree, which is then believed to represent the actual historical relationships between various population groups, is called the maximum parsimony tree.

According to one of the original African Eve reports, written in 1987 by Cann, Stoneking, and Wilson,[21] researchers found that the maximum parsimony tree had the African group at its root. Another report in 1991 by Vigilant, Stoneking, Harpending, Hawkes, and Wilson confirmed this analysis.[22]

However, not everything is as clear-cut as it sounds. Geneticist Alan Templeton points out that by rerunning the data gathered in the first analysis, other scientists found 10,000 trees that were more parsimonious than the tree originally presented as the maximum parsimony tree. Many of these trees had mixed Asian-African roots.[23] Analyzing the second report, Templeton himself found 1,000 trees that were more parsimonious than the one claimed to be the most parsimonious. All these were rooted in non-African populations. According to Templeton, so much for the African Eve theory.[24]

Why such different results? Alan Templeton explains: "Computer programs ... cannot guarantee that the maximum parsimony tree will be found when dealing with such large data sets as these because the state space is too large to search exhaustively."[25] He pointed out that in one of the studies there were 1.68×10^{294} possible trees. It is beyond the capacity of any computer to exhaust even a fraction of such a large space. What the computers do instead is to pick out a tree that is maximally parsimonious only within a subset of the total number of possible trees. Which subset is used depends in turn on the order in which the data was fed into the computer. In order to circumvent the computer's choice, scientists randomly feed the same data into the computer several times. When this has been done a sufficient number of times and a number of parsimonious trees has been established, one can compare them and arrive at a conclusion. For the original African Eve studies, a less thorough method was followed.

What's more, according to Templeton, even the data randomization doesn't actually solve the problem. These studies involve a number of assumptions that are hard to verify and may turn out to be incorrect – for example, that mitochondrial DNA is not subject to natural selection. In fact, studies now show this to be untrue. It has also been assumed that all the regions studied had about the same population growth, but this too may not necessarily be so. The data can be misleading if populations in different regions have mixed, which very well may be the case. All in all, according to Templeton, it is not possible through such studies alone to reach an absolute conclusion about where the first common human ancestor lived.

And as the geographical location of the last common female ancestor of all human beings is questionable, so is the date (200,000 years ago) said to determine her age. Again, this date is dependent on having a number of assumptions prove true – for example, the date when the human and chimpanzee line split. Some say this took place four million years ago, others six, nine, or even ten million years ago. (Of course, this assumes that humans and chimpanzees have a common ancestor in the first place!) To some this would seem like trying to prove common ancestry by assuming common ancestry, which is circular reasoning. In any case, when each of these numbers is put into the formula, the 200,000 years can easily stretch into as much as 1.3 million years.[26]

Another factor calculated into this date estimate is the "molecular clock," or the rate of mutation. In the calculation currently used, geneticists work under the assumption that mitochondrial DNA is not affected by natural selection, but, as already mentioned, it *is* apparently selected for. Several other factors affect the calculation of the age of this last common female ancestor so much that in one study, and in light of the many uncertainties, researchers arrived at an age for the first common human ancestor at somewhere between 33,000 and 675,000 years ago.[27]

All in all, it is not unreasonable to consider studies of mitochondrial DNA and other genetic studies used to determine human ancestry and age ambiguous at best and misleading at worst; they are based on so many assumptions that at one point Oxford University population geneticist Rosalind Harding had to admit, "There's no clear genetic test. We're going to have to let the fossil people answer this one."[28]

All this leads us to the next chapter, where we'll have a real fossil-man, Dr. Michael Cremo, give his bid on human prehistory.

CHAPTER 9

Human Origins and the Archeological Record

Michael A. Cremo

E volutionists say that hominins, the biological group that includes today's humans and their supposed ape-man ancestors, split off from the African apes around six million years ago. From some of these early hominins came *Australopithecus.* There are, we are told, many species of *Australopithecus,* the earliest of which came into existence about four or five million years ago. From one of them arose *Homo habilis,* allegedly the first toolmaker. Next came *Homo erectus,* allegedly the first hominin to use fire. Then came early modern humans and the Neanderthals. Finally, anatomically modern humans arrived on the scene between 100,000 years and 200,000 years ago. It all sounds so perfectly clear when you hear a teacher say it, when you read it in a book, or when you see it in a museum display or on television.

But over the past 150 years, archeologists and other earth scientists have discovered many human bones, footprints, and artifacts that contradict the evolutionary account of human origins. This evidence shows that anatomically modern humans existed millions of years ago. If accepted, this evidence would destroy the evolutionary scenario outlined above, which has anatomically modern humans emerging about 100,000 years ago. *Australopithecus, Homo habilis, Homo erectus,* and the Neanderthals would no longer be human ancestors. They would all simply be creatures that coexisted with anatomically modern humans. I documented the evidence that contradicts the accepted theory of human evolution in the book *Forbidden Archeology* along with my coauthor Richard Thompson. The evidence is not very well known because of a process of knowledge filtration that operates in the world of science. When I am speaking about knowledge filtration, I am not talking about a satanic conspiracy to suppress truth. Rather I am speaking about something that philosophers and historians of science have understood for a long time: Theoretical preconceptions influence the treatment of evidence in science. In an ideal world, theories would be adjusted to fit new evidence, but in the real world we find that sometimes evidence is rejected to preserve theories in which scientists have a lot of faith.

We will now consider just a few of the many hundreds of examples from the book.

Human Footprints

In 1979, at a place called Laetoli, in the country of Tanzania in East Africa, Mary Leakey and her colleagues discovered footprints in solidified volcanic ash deposits over 3.7 million years old. Mary Leakey[1] and others said the prints were indistinguishable from those of modern humans. Of course, Mary Leakey, being an evolutionist, did not believe humans like us existed 3.7 million years ago. So how did she explain the footprints? She proposed that the ape-men that existed at that time, called *Australopithecus,* had feet just like those of modern human beings. But according to other scientists, such as physical anthropologist R. H. Tuttle of the University of Chicago, fossil foot bones of the known australopithecines of 3.6 million years ago show they had feet that were distinctly apelike.[2] Hence they were incompatible with the Laetoli prints. The only creature known to science today that has a foot exactly like that of a modern human being is in fact a modern human being. So what did Mary Leakey actually find? It appears she found evidence that humans like us existed 3.7 million years ago.

Stone Tools

In the 1960s, anthropologists uncovered advanced stone tools at Hueyatlaco, Mexico. Geologist Virginia Steen-McIntyre and her colleagues, using four different dating methods (uranium series, fission track, tephra hydration, and stratigraphic analysis), obtained an age of about 250,000 years for the site's implement-bearing layers.[3] Evolutionists now believe that humans capable of making the kind of tools found at Hueyatlaco came into existence between 100,000 and 200,000 years ago in Africa. Furthermore, they believe that humans entered North America only about 20,000 years ago.

Virginia Steen-McIntyre experienced difficulty in getting her dating study on Hueyatlaco published. "The problem as I see it is much bigger than Hueyatlaco," she wrote on March 30, 1981 to Estella Leopold, associate editor of *Quaternary Research*. "It concerns the manipulation of scientific thought through the suppression of 'Enigmatic Data,' data that challenges the prevailing mode of thinking. Hueyatlaco certainly does that! Not being an anthropologist, I didn't realize the full significance of our dates back in 1973, nor how deeply woven into our thought the current theory of human evolution has become. Our work at Hueyatlaco has been rejected by most archeologists because it contradicts that theory, period."[4] This pattern of data suppression has been going on for a long time.

In 1880, J. D. Whitney, the state geologist of California, published a lengthy review[5] of advanced stone tools found in California gold mines. The implements, including spear points and stone mortars and pestles, were found deep in mine shafts, underneath thick, undisturbed layers of lava. According to modern geological reports, the formations in which the objects were found are from 9 million to over 55 million years old.[6] W. H. Holmes of the Smithsonian Institution, one of the most vocal critics of the California finds, wrote: "Perhaps if Professor

Whitney had fully appreciated the story of human evolution as it is understood today, he would have hesitated to announce the conclusions formulated [that humans existed in very ancient times in North America], notwithstanding the imposing array of testimony with which he was confronted."[7] In other words, if the facts do not agree with the favored theory, then such facts, even an imposing array of them, had to be discarded. And that's what happened.

But some of the artifacts from the California gold mines are still in the collection of the Museum of Anthropology of the University of California at Berkeley. In 1996 I was a consultant for the television special "The Mysterious Origins of Man," produced by Bill Cote for the American television network NBC. On my advice, Cote approached the museum officials for permission to see and film the artifacts, but permission was denied. We were, however, able to find photographs of some of the artifacts included by Whitney in his original report, and used those for the program. When Darwinist scientists in the United States found that NBC was going to air the program they tried to stop this from happening. When they failed to stop NBC from showing the program a second time, some of these scientists approached the Federal Communications Commission and asked the FCC to investigate, censure, and fine NBC for having shown the program.[8]

In 2005 I returned to the Museum of Anthropology at Berkeley and received permission from the staff to study and photograph some of the artifacts from the California gold mines for a paper I presented at a meeting of the World Archaeological Congress, the world's largest international organization of archeologists.

Evidence for Advanced Culture in Distant Ages

The above-mentioned evidence gives the impression that humans from the distant past had a very low level of material culture. But artifacts suggestive of more developed cultural and technological achievement have also been found. Here are a few examples.

In 1871, William E. Dubois of the Smithsonian Institution reported on a copper coin from Lawn Ridge, in Marshall County, Illinois. One side of the coin showed some human figures and markings in an unknown script. The object came from a well boring, at a depth of 114 feet.[9] Using the drilling record, the Illinois State Geological Survey estimated the age of the deposits at the 114-foot level. The deposits would have formed during the Yarmouthian interglacial period "sometime between 200,000 and 400,000 years ago."[10] The coin suggests the existence of a civilization at least 200,000 years ago in North America. Yet beings intelligent enough to make and use coins (*Homo sapiens sapiens*) are generally not thought to have lived much earlier than 100,000 years ago. According to standard views, metal coins were first used in Asia Minor during the eighth century BC.

A small human image, skillfully formed in clay, was found in 1889 at Nampa, Idaho. The figurine came from the 300-foot level of a well boring.[11] Responding to inquiries by my research assistant, the United States Geological Survey stated in a letter that the layer at a depth of over 300 feet is "probably of the Glenns Ferry Formation, upper Idaho Group, which is generally considered to be of Plio-Pleistocene age." The boundary between the Pliocene and the Pleistocene lies at 2 million years ago. Other than *Homo sapiens sapiens*, no hominid is known to have fashioned works of art like the Nampa figurine. The evidence therefore suggests that humans of the modern type were living in America around 2 million years ago.

> **The evidence therefore suggests that humans of the modern type were living in America around 2 million years ago.**

In his book *Mineralogy,* Count Bournon recorded an intriguing discovery made by French workmen in the latter part of the eighteenth century.[12] The workmen, who were quarrying limestone near Aix-en-Provence, had gone through eleven layers of limestone separated by layers of sediments. Then, in the clayey sand above the twelfth layer, Bournon said "they found stumps of columns and fragments of stone half wrought, and the stone was exactly similar to that of the quarry:

they found moreover coins, handles of hammers, and other tools or fragments of tools in wood." The wood artifacts were petrified. The limestones of Aix-en-Provence are from the Oligocene,[13] which means the objects found in the limestones could be 24–36 million years old.

According to a report published in *Scientific American* (1852), a beautiful metallic vase, with silver inlaid floral patterns, came from fifteen

feet deep in a layer of solid rock in Dorchester, Massachusetts. According to a recent U.S. Geological Survey map of the Boston-Dorchester area, the rock at that location, at that depth (the Roxbury conglomerate), is of Precambrian age, over 600 million years old.

Extremely Old Human Fossils

As we have seen, there are footprints, stone tools, and other artifacts showing a human presence going back millions of years. But are there also any human fossils to further support this conclusion? The answer is yes.

In the 1890s Eugene Dubois found an apelike skullcap and a thigh-bone, or femur, at Trinil, in Java. Although the femur was found about forty-five feet from the skull, Dubois believed that both the skull and the femur belonged to the same creature. These were the first discover-ies of the ape-man now called *Homo erectus*. However, scientists later showed that the femur found along with the skull is unlike other *Homo erectus* femurs that were found afterwards and that it exactly resembles modern human femurs.[14] They have thus concluded that the femur does not belong with the skull. But what then do we make of the femur? Both the femur and the skull were found in a formation about 800,000 years old.[15] It would appear, therefore, that we now have evidence for anatomically modern humans in Java at about 800,000 years ago.

In 1972 the ER 1481 femur (thighbone) was found at Lake Turkana, Kenya, by John Harris in layers of rock about 1.8 million years old. Richard Leakey described[16] this femur as almost indistinguishable from that of a modern human being. He attributed it to the ape-man *Homo habilis*. But the ER 1481 was found all by itself, not connected with other bones. Later, when other researchers found a fairly complete skeleton of *Homo habilis* at Olduvai Gorge, they found its femur was quite small and was not like that of a modern human being.[17] This sug-gests that the ER 1481 femur did not belong to *Homo habilis*. Instead, it appears that we have in the ER 1481 femur evidence that humans like us lived about 1.8 million years ago.

Several other bones described as being like those of anatomically modern humans were found at other sites in Africa, including: a humerus (upper arm bone) found in 1965 at Kanapoi, Kenya, and given an age of about 4 million years;[18] a humerus from Gombore, Ethiopia, reported in 1977[19] and given an age of about 1.5 million years; and an ankle bone (talus) found at East Rudolf, Kenya, in 1974[20] and given an age of about 2 million years.

Further evidence for anatomically modern humans existing in very early times comes from Argentina. In 1896, workers excavating a dry dock in Buenos Aires found a human skull. They took it from the rudder pit at the bottom of the excavation, after breaking through a layer of a hard, limestonelike substance called *tosca*. The level at which the skull was found was 11 meters (36 feet) below the bed of the river La Plata.[21] According to Ales Hrdlička of the Smithsonian Institution, the skull was just like that of modern humans.[22] The skull was found in what Hrdlička called "the upper-most portion of the Pre-Ensenadean stratum."[23] According to modern geological opinion, the Pre-Ensenadean stratum is at least 1 to 1.5 million years old.[24] Hrdlička, being an evolutionist, thought that just because the skull was modern in form it could not be genuinely old, but the evidence suggests that the skull is not only modern in form but is also over a million years old.

In 1913, Dr. Hans Reck, of Berlin University, found an anatomically modern human skeleton in Bed II of Olduvai Gorge. This would make the anatomically modern skeleton over 1 million years old. Aware of the possibility of intrusive burial, Reck carefully examined the sediments around the skeleton and determined that there was absolutely no sign of disturbance.[25] During World War II, most of the skeleton was lost. After the war, Reiner Protsch (1974) did a carbon 14 test on some small fragments of bone he thought belonged to the skeleton. This test gave an age of about 17,000 years.[26] But there are several problems with this date. First of all, it is not clear that the bone fragments he tested really belonged to Reck's skeleton. Second, even if the bone fragments did belong to Reck's skeleton, they could have been contaminated with recent carbon during the several decades they had lain exposed in the museum. This would have caused the carbon 14 test to yield a falsely young date. Third, Reiner Protsch was later removed from his university position when it became known that he had falsified numerous radiocarbon dates.[27] Thus it would appear there is no good reason to assign the skeleton an age different from that of the layer in which it was found, which would make it over 1 million years old.

In 1855, a human jaw was discovered at Foxhall, England, by workers digging in a quarry. Robert H. Collyer, an American physician then residing in London, acquired the fossil. He noted that the bed from which the jaw was said to have been taken was sixteen feet below the surface, in the Red Crag Formation.[28] The condition of the jaw, thoroughly infiltrated with iron oxide, was consistent with incorporation in this bed. The 16-foot level of the Red Crag Formation at Foxhall is the same from which J. Reid Moir[29] later recovered stone tools and signs of fire. Anything found in the Red Crag formation would be at least 2.5 million years old.[30]

In December of 1879 a landowner at Castenedolo, Italy, noticed some human bones in an excavation. Professor Giuseppe Ragazzoni, a geologist at the Technical Institute of Brescia, traveled to Castenedolo and collected the bones, which included pieces of the skull, some teeth, and parts of the backbone, ribs, arms, legs, and feet. More bones were found over the next few weeks. On February 16 a complete skeleton was discovered. Ragazzoni journeyed to the site and supervised the excavation. The skeleton, enveloped in a mass of blue clay, turned out to be that of an anatomically modern human female. "The skeleton," said Ragazzoni, "was found in the middle of the layer of blue clay.... The stratum of blue clay, which is over 1 meter [3 feet] thick, has preserved its uniform stratification, and does not show any sign of disturbance."[31] He added, "The skeleton was very likely deposited in a kind of marine mud and not buried at a later time, for in this case one would have been able to detect traces of the overlying yellow sand and the iron-red clay called *ferretto*." Modern geologists place the blue clays at Castenedolo in the Astian stage of the Middle Pliocene, which would give the discoveries from Castenedolo an age of about 3 to 4 million years. A carbon 14 test yielded an age of 958 years for some of the Castenedolo bones.[33] But the methods employed are now considered unreliable. And the bones themselves, which had been sitting in a museum for almost 90 years, were very likely contaminated with recent carbon, causing the test to yield a falsely young age.

Another Pliocene find comes from Savona, a town on the Italian Riviera, about 30 miles west of Genoa. In the 1850s, while constructing a church, workmen discovered an anatomically modern human skeleton at the bottom of a trench 3 meters (10 feet) deep. The layer containing the skeleton was the same age as the layer containing the skeletons at Castenedolo,[34] i.e. Middle Pliocene, about 3 to 4 million years old. Arthur Issel communicated details of the Savona find to the members of the International Congress of Prehistoric Anthropology and Archeology at Paris in 1867.[35] He declared that the Savona human "was contemporary with the strata in which he was found." [36] Some suggested the skeleton was recently buried in the place where it was found. But a report given at the International Congress of Prehistoric Anthropology and Archeology at Bologna in 1871 said: "Had it been a burial we would expect to find the upper layers mixed with the lower. The upper layers contain white quartzite sands. The result of mixing would have been the definite lightening of a closely circumscribed region of the Pliocene clay sufficient to cause some doubts in the spectators that it was genuinely ancient, as they affirmed. The biggest and smallest cavities of the human bones are filled with compacted Pliocene clay. This could only have happened when the clay was in a muddy consistency, during Pliocene times."[37] Deo Gratias pointed out that the clay was now hard and dry. Also, the skeleton was found at a depth of 3 meters (10 feet), rather deep for a burial.

We have already discussed the numerous stone implements discovered in the gold-bearing gravels of the Sierra Nevada Mountains of California. Human bones were also found in these gravels, which range from 33 million to 55 million years old. On January 1, 1873, the president of the Boston Society of Natural History read extracts from a letter by Dr. C. F. Winslow about a discovery of human bones at Table Mountain in Tuolumne County, California. One find was made in 1855 or 1856, and the details were communicated to Winslow by Capt. David B. Akey, who had witnessed it. Winslow[38] gave this account of Akey's testimony: "He states that in a tunnel run into the mountain ... a complete human skeleton was found and taken out by miners personally known to him.... He thinks that the depth from the surface at which this skeleton was found was two hundred feet, and from one hundred and eighty to two hundred feet from the opening cut or face of the tunnel. The bones were in a moist condition, found among the gravel and very near the bedrock." The gold-bearing gravel above the bedrock, where the skeleton was found, is between 33 and 55 million years old.[39] This must be the age of the skeleton unless it was introduced into the gravels at a later time, and we are not aware of any evidence indicating such an intrusion. In 1857, a fragment of human skull was found in a mineshaft, in the gold-bearing gravels below the lava cap of Table Mountain. The skull fragment was later given to Winslow, who sent it to the Boston Society of Natural History. Another fragment from the same skull was sent to the Museum of the Philadelphia Academy of Natural Sciences. The lava cap of Table Mountain is 9 million years old. The oldest gravels below the lava are 55 million years old. The skull fragments could thus be from 9 million to 55 million years old.

Finally, the following brief but intriguing report appeared in a journal called *The Geologist:* "In Macoupin County, Illinois, the bones of a man were recently found on a coal-bed capped with two feet of slate rock, ninety feet below the surface of the earth…. The bones, when found, were covered with a crust or coating of hard glossy matter, as black as coal itself, but when scraped away left the bones white and natural."[40] My research assistant Stephen Bernath received a letter[41] from C. Brian Trask of the Illinois State Geological Survey informing us that the coal bed at that location is from the upper Pennsylvanian system. Therefore the coal bed upon which the Macoupin County skeleton was found is at least 286 million years old and might be as much as 320 million years old.

Readers may notice that some of these discoveries contradicting the current theories of human evolution come from the nineteenth century. There are two things about this we need to keep in mind. First, many of the discoveries that established the current theories of human evolution, and which are still present in today's textbooks, also come from the nineteenth century. The first Neanderthal skeletons were discovered in the nineteenth century. The first *Homo erectus* skeletons were discovered in the nineteenth century. Also, in the nineteenth century the timeline of human evolution had not been very firmly established, so discoveries of evidence for extreme human antiquity were given serious consideration and were often published by scientists in mainstream scientific publications. Today, with the timeline of human evolution more firmly established, scientists are more likely to be suspicious of discoveries that contradict their current understandings. Nevertheless, many examples of archeological evidence for extreme human antiquity come from the more recent history of archeology.

Conclusion

The evidence documented in *Forbidden Archeology* demonstrates that we genuinely need an alternative to the Darwinian picture of human evolution. Even confining ourselves to physical evidence in the form of fossils and artifacts, an evolutionary picture fails to emerge. The explanation that best fits the facts is that humans like ourselves and other more or less humanlike beings have coexisted on this planet for hundreds of millions of years.

CHAPTER 10

The Fine-tuned Universe

This chapter discusses cosmology. One might ask, What is the link between cosmology and Darwin's theory of evolution? The answer is that although Darwin's theory deals only with life as it is found here on earth, Darwinism is just one part of the greater attempt by materialists to explain all phenomena in terms of matter. As it turns out, intelligent design arguments can similarly be extended beyond biology.

Proponents of intelligent design point to the anthropological principle, or how the universe appears to have been designed for life – a topic within the realm of cosmology. That the universe does seem to have telltale features that point to an intelligent cause has implications for our understanding of life on earth. Kenneth E. Boulding, former president of the American Association for the Advancement of Science, wrote, "Cosmology ... is likely to be very insecure, simply because it studies a very large

Kenneth E. Boulding

universe with a small and biased sample."[1] These words aptly describe how almost everything about the research into the structure of the universe may turn out to be imperfect or even fundamentally wrong. Like small insects looking up at the night sky from the bottom of a well, we are looking out into a gigantic universe from one small corner of it. From here we can see only a small fraction of the totality of space. Our perspective is also quite limited when it comes to time. The universe has existed for billions of years; the recorded history of humans, by comparison, has taken place over a split second.

How little we actually know can be illustrated by "dark matter" and "dark energy," a topic cosmologists have been discussing now for more than a decade. These refer, we are told, to matter and energy that exist in a form that has so far escaped detection. We know only that it *must* be there because it's the only way to account for the expansion of the universe. It is now thought that more than 90 percent of all matter and energy are undetectable. Some cosmologists speculate that this matter and energy may even be organized into other-dimensional worlds – worlds to which we have no access from our dimension. Other cosmologists contest the notion of dark matter and dark energy: there is really no hard evidence that they exist.

Other major assumptions underlying modern cosmology may even be radically wrong. For example, think of the concept of uniformity – the idea that physical laws are identical, and have always been identical, everywhere in the universe. While this assumption is reasonable, there is no way to test it. One can reason in favor of uniformity if one assumes that particles of matter and energy, and the forces that operate in space and time between them, are all there is. However, if something more is at work – for example, if the consciousness plays a fundamental part in the world or if there is a creator – then the assumption of uniformity may be untrue. If the laws of nature are only secondary causes of creation set in motion by a creator, it is possible that that same creator may contravene his own laws as he sees fit. If this were the case, then everything we now believe to be true about the universe may be flawed.

Still, some interesting facts have nevertheless come out of cosmological research over the last few decades. Today, almost all cosmologists accept a form of the Big Bang theory, which states that the universe started from a point with practically infinite density and an infinitely high temperature. Initially, when the idea of the Big Bang was first introduced, many scientists resisted the idea of the universe having a beginning at all. This hesitation was partly caused by anti-religious biases: a universe with a beginning invariably points to a creator. So until a few decades ago the most favored theory was the steady state theory, or the idea that the universe has always existed. However, certain observations have convinced most scientists that the universe is indeed expanding and that it began at some point in time.

It has apparently been fourteen billion years since the Big Bang. At its beginning the universe is said to have been filled with a superheated plasma that condensed into subatomic particles when it expanded and cooled. Wherever matter and energy were concentrated, galaxies and stars formed. In the cores of these superheated stars heavier elements were produced. When the stars burned out and exploded as supernovae, even heavier elements formed in the supernovae's shock and heat waves.

What is particularly interesting to note is that the Big Bang model of the universe reveals a number of physical constants that are so precise that if they were only fractionally smaller or larger there would be no stable atoms, stars, galaxies, and none of the elementary particles necessary for life. The values of these constants appear arbitrary; that is, there is no inherent quality or property in nature that determines them. They just *happen* to be perfect. The probability that this perfection could be the result of pure chance is beyond exceedingly small. Has the universe been designed for life? Many cosmologists are now asking themselves this question.[2]

Electromagnetism and Gravity

Two important forces in the universe are gravity and electromagnetism. Atoms are made of subatomic particles with negatively charged electrons and positively charged protons. The electromagnetic attraction between them keeps the atoms together.

Gravity also acts within the atom, but its effect is so weak that for all practical purposes it has no effect at all. On the other hand, gravity has a very real effect on larger objects. When atoms combine and form large bodies of matter, gravity increases proportionally. At the same time, the electromagnetic forces inside the atoms have little or no influence on larger bodies because the negative and positive forces within the atoms neutralize one another. The ratio between the electromagnetic and gravitational forces operating within an atom is called N. In our universe N has a value of 10^{36}. In other words, the electromagnetic attraction between the electron and the proton is 10^{36} times greater than the gravitational attraction between them. Why does N have *exactly* this value? Sir Martin Rees writes in *Just Six Numbers*, "We have no theory that tells us the value of N. All we know is that nothing as complex as humankind could have emerged if N was much less than 1,000,000,000,000,000,000,000,000,000,000,000,000 [10^{36}]."[3]

> **If the binding energy had been just a little smaller or larger there would have been universal consequences.**

If, for example, N had been 10^{30} instead of 10^{36}, then a million times fewer atoms could have formed a star. Stars supposedly arise when the gravitational attraction in hydrogen and helium clouds causes them to condense. As gas condenses it becomes warmer until it incites nuclear fusion reactions. The heat from the fusion pushes the matter away from the center of the star, while gravity pulls the matter toward it. A stable star is a result of a balance between these expansions and contractions.

The star needs to have enough gas to contract and to start a fusion process, and it must preserve enough of its matter to keep the heat energy from hurling all the matter into outer space. Normally stars need to be quite large to accomplish this. However, if gravity were stronger, the fusion process could have started with less atoms. Similarly, fewer atoms would have been needed to counteract the outward expansion. If N had been 10^{30} instead of 10^{36}, a millionth as many atoms would have been enough. The stars would have been much smaller and burned their nuclear fuel a lot faster. Their average life span would have been 10,000 years instead of their current ten billion, which of course would have had implications for biological life as we know it.

The Binding Energy

The figure associated with binding energy is another important number. Different atoms have different binding energies. The most important is the binding energy of hydrogen. According to cosmologists, hydrogen is the first element – formed immediately after the Big Bang. The rest of the elements form as hydrogen is transformed through the fusion reactions in stars.

The first generation of stars in the universe is said to have first converted all its hydrogen into helium. The nucleus of hydrogen contains one proton. Some hydrogen nuclei also bind a neutron to a proton and form the hydrogen isotope deuterium. When two deuterium nuclei are forced to fuse, they form helium, with its two protons and two neutrons. Then something interesting takes place. Normally, when two balls each weighing one gram are fused, the new ball will weigh two grams. But here, although made up of two deuterium nuclei, the newly formed helium nucleus somehow weighs less than the two deuterium nuclei. More precisely, it has a mass of only 0.993 – that is, only 99.3% of the mass of the two deuterium nuclei. What happened to the missing mass of 0.007 (0.7%)? It has been transformed into energy during fusion. This number, 0.007, is the binding energy, which is directly related to the strong nuclear force that keeps the protons in the nucleus of the atom together. Protons normally repel one another just as the positive poles of two magnets repel one another, but the strong nuclear force counteracts this repulsion and holds the protons together in the nucleus.

If this binding energy had been just a little smaller or larger there would have been universal consequences. If, for example, the binding energy had been 0.006 instead of 0.007, elements heavier than hydrogen could not have formed. Heavier elements are formed by adding protons to an atom's nucleus. Iron has twenty-six protons. To form iron or any heavier element, one first has to form helium from hydrogen. The helium nucleus has two protons and two neutrons. Getting from hydrogen to helium requires an intermediate stage where hydrogen is changed into deuterium, which contains one proton and one neutron. Only then is it possible for two deuterium nuclei to fuse and form a helium atom with its two protons and two neutrons.

If the binding energy had been 0.006 instead of 0.007, the strong nuclear force could not have bound a neutron to a proton, and so it would have been impossible for either deuterium or helium to form. The universe, it seems, would have forever consisted only of hydrogen atoms.

It would have been equally problematic if the binding energy had been 0.008. A strong nuclear force is necessary to bind protons, but a binding energy of 0.007 is not strong enough to accomplish the task. However, a binding energy of 0.007 *is* strong enough to bind a proton to a neutron and thus to form deuterium – after which two deuterium isotopes can form helium. If the binding energy had been 0.008 or more, the strong nuclear force would have been strong enough to bind two protons. Combined, the two protons would have formed a diproton. All the hydrogen atoms in the early universe would have then turned into diprotons. As it so happens, only a portion of the universe's hydrogen atoms actually become helium over long periods of time, leaving enough hydrogen to form the many hydrogen compounds crucial to life – water (H_2O), for example. A binding energy of 0.008 or more would actually have left the universe without water.

The Resonant Energy Level

When the first stars ran out of hydrogen, their helium core condensed, causing the stars' temperature to rise, which in turn caused the helium to fuse into carbon. A helium nucleus has two protons, and a carbon nucleus has six. Three helium nuclei can, in principle, fuse to form a carbon nucleus, but it is highly improbable that three helium nuclei will collide simultaneously in the precise way necessary for them to form carbon. Thus nature has arranged a two-step process. First, two helium nuclei fuse to form a beryllium nucleus with four protons, whereupon a beryllium nucleus combines with one more helium nucleus to form carbon. However, the beryllium nucleus is very unstable and quickly splits back into helium nuclei. One would therefore not expect that carbon would have formed to the extent it did, as is currently observed in the universe. However, British astronomer Sir Fred Hoyle discovered that carbon has a surprisingly favorable "resonant energy level," which when combined with the heat at a star's core allows beryllium and helium to combine more willingly than they would otherwise have done in beryllium's short life span. Since carbon is the most important element in organic life, one can understand how important this circumstance is.

Oxygen, another important element, is the next to be formed. Most of the carbon should have quickly become oxygen when the carbon nuclei combined with one more helium nucleus (oxygen has eight protons), but oxygen just happens to have a resonant energy level that makes this reaction less frequent. This fortunate circumstance allows enough carbon to remain in the universe to form carbon-based life. A difference of even 4% in the resonant energy level of oxygen would have burned up all the carbon.

The Original Mass Distribution

If the gas cloud after the Big Bang had been a perfect sphere, then all the atoms would have distributed themselves equally. In order for stars, galaxies, and clusters of galaxies to have formed there must have been irregularities in the distribution of matter. This means that matter had to have been slightly denser in some areas than others. In these more compacted areas the atoms attracted one another through gravitational pull and became stars and galaxies.

The number for this uneven distribution of matter is called Q. Scientists have calculated Q at 10^{-5}. It turns out that 10^{-5} is the only number which would have resulted in stable stars and planets. What if Q were smaller than 10^{-5}? According to Sir Martin Rees, again in his book *Just Six Numbers:* "The resultant galaxies would be anaemic structures in which star formation would be slow and inefficient, and 'processed' material would be blown out of the galaxy rather than being recycled into new stars that could form planetary systems."[4] If Q were smaller than 10^{-5} – perhaps 10^{-6} – "[the] gas would never condense into gravitationally bound structures at all, and such a universe would forever remain dark and featureless."[5]

But what if Q were bigger than 10^{-5}? Rees says that in such a universe most matter would have quickly collapsed into black holes. Whatever stars remained would have been "packed too close together and buffeted too frequently to retain stable planetary systems."[6]

Although a 10^{-5} Q is critical for existence, there is no special reason why Q has this value. Rees: "The way Q is determined … is still perplexing."[7]

How Can We Explain This?

There are other critical values in the universe, such as the anti-gravitational force. This force was discovered in the 1990s and works in a way opposite to gravitation. It must also have a precise value; a value a little greater or smaller would have caused the universe to collapse immediately after the Big Bang.

What has caused this apparently precise fine-tuning of physical constants? What has caused the rare circumstances that surround the earth?

Some have proposed the multiverse theory, which states that new universes are constantly coming into being. Each of these new universes has different values for their physical constants; our universe just happens to have the right values to allow life as we know it.

But some cosmologists claim this precision indicates an intelligent designer. The fine-tuning of the universe cannot be explained away as mere chance. More than anything it appears to be the arrangement of intelligence. As British astronomer Sir Fred Hoyle remarked, "I do not believe that any scientist who examines the evidence would fail to draw the inference that the laws of physics have been deliberately designed with regard to the consequences they produce inside the stars."[8]

CHAPTER 11

Consciousness, Near-death Experiences, and Reincarnation

S o far I have argued that particular features of physical nature may point to something beyond the physical. I have discussed the insufficiency of material processes to account for every aspect of a living organism and of the universe itself, and have pointed to suggestions of an intelligence behind nature, an intelligence most people call "God." Nevertheless, I have not yet examined any evidence for the nonmaterial; I have simply looked at the standard material evidence given in the study of mainstream physics, chemistry, and biology.

This and the following two chapters will now take us a step further by presenting arguments for the reality of phenomena in nature that are clearly nonmaterial. Although we will remain within the realm of the empirical – that which can be perceived by the senses and thus subjected to scientific experimentation and scrutiny – I would like to show how nature has aspects to it that cannot be ascribed or reduced to an interaction between matter and energy. We will begin by looking at consciousness.

All of us can perceive ourselves; that is, we perceive that we exist. Self-awareness is a common and immediate experience. But what is consciousness?

Before you answer this question, I would like you to imagine yourself lying in bed tonight, under the blankets, with your eyes closed. As on other nights, you remain partially awake for a while, perhaps remembering what happened to you during the course of your day. Then, without realizing it, imperceptibly you fall asleep. At that point you leave your waking world and enter a dream. In your dream you have forgotten all about your daytime identity. Yet your dream experience, with all its joys and fears, feels just as real as your waking reality. You might imagine you are having a nightmare. Perhaps you are being chased by a tiger. The terror you experience in your dream is no different from the terror you would feel if you were awake being chased by a real tiger. You run. You glance backwards and see that the tiger is almost upon you. It jumps ...

And then you awake. A feeling of relief washes over you. It was only a dream! The tiger wasn't real, and in this, your real life, you are safe. You remember where you are, who you are, what's going on in your life. You're grateful for reality.

But wait a minute. Is your waking experience real? What *is* reality? What makes us think that our waking life is real and our dream life unreal? The experience we have in dreams certainly *feels* real – just as real as any waking experience. The only reason we consider dreams unreal is that they quickly begin and end. If a dream never ended, it wouldn't be a dream – it would be our reality.

People throughout the world have been exploring these ideas for centuries, and we encounter such ideas in the world's greatest books of wisdom. For example, the *Bhagavad-gita,* India's guidebook on consciousness and reality, defines reality as something unchangeable, unreality as something that has both a beginning and an end. Let's work with this definition for a moment: If we are born and die, then the experiences we have in this lifetime – are they real? The dreams we have while we sleep may last only a few moments and the waking state hours at a time, but since at death we leave our waking experience behind, isn't it as unreal as a dream?

I have presented these ideas to audiences many times. At this point I usually stop and ask my listeners, "So what is – or *where* is – reality in the midst of all this? If we define reality as something without beginning and end, something constant and changeless, then what is real about *your* life?" It's rare that someone can answer this question, but when people do, they usually say, "According to this definition, everything is unreal. There is no reality."

But there *is* one constant and unchangeable element in you that permeates your life. You, the *conscious observer,* change neither when you are awake nor when asleep. Although during a dream you may forget your waking identity and the activities you usually perform while awake, you are still present, witnessing the dream. When you awake, your dream fades, and instead you witness your waking life.[1]

The example of the waking and dream states as pointers to the existence of the conscious observer has been constructed from one of the *Bhagavad-gita's* basic teachings, which explains that the consciousness, the "self," is both constant and unchangeable. This indicates, of course, that it is also eternal and nonmaterial, since all matter is subject to destruction. According to the *Bhagavad-gita,* there is an essential difference between the body and the self, for the body is ever changing but "I" remain the same. I can remember when "I" was five, ten, twenty years old. The bodies "I" had at each of those times have disappeared – hardly a molecule remains with me from cradle to grave – yet "I" remain. Therefore, "I" and the body must be different.[2]

The ancient Greeks formed a similar argument to explain the eternality of the witness-self, and the concept is central to Plato's *Phaedo,* which presents Socrates' last dialogue. Socrates was sentenced by the Athens parliament to die by drinking hemlock. On the morning of his execution day, his friends begged him to save himself – they had worked out a plot to free him from prison – but Socrates argued that escape was both morally wrong and spiritually unnecessary. After all, the self is eternal and cannot be killed. In the course of the conversation his friends contested the notion of the eternality of the self, giving Socrates room to argue his view:

> We ought, I think, to ask ourselves this: What sort of thing is it that would naturally suffer the fate of being dispersed? For what sort of thing should we fear this fate, and for what should we not? When we have answered this, we should next consider to which class the soul [or self] belongs, and then we shall know whether to feel confidence or fear about the fate of our souls.

Socrates goes on to discuss the difference between an object that is a composite of other objects, and an "incomposite," as he calls it. A composite object is variable and inconstant in nature, whereas an incomposite object is constant and invariable. He speaks to his friend Cebes:

> **Socrates:** Very well, then, in the light of all that we have said, both now and before, to which class do you think that the soul bears the closer resemblance and relation?
>
> **Cebes:** I think, Socrates, that even the dullest person would agree, from this line of reasoning, that the soul is in every possible way more like the invariable than the variable.
>
> **Socrates:** And the body?
>
> **Cebes:** To the other.[3]

What Socrates is saying is that consciousness must be nonphysical because it is unchanging. This unchanging consciousness is the symptom of an eternal self (or soul), just as heat and light are symptoms of fire. The proposal that an eternal conscious self inhabits the temporary physical body is a simple and direct explanation for consciousness.

Yet many scientists today are not ready to accept such a proposal. At the same time, although these scientists generally assume that consciousness is caused by physical processes in the brain, some admit that consciousness is one of biology's great unsolved mysteries. Philosopher Jerry Fodor wrote in 1992, "Nobody has the slightest idea how anything material could be conscious. Nobody even knows what it would be like to have the slightest idea about how anything material could be conscious."[4]

According to psychologist Stuart Sutherland, "Consciousness is a fascinating but elusive phenomenon; it is impossible to specify what it is, what it does, or why it evolved. Nothing worth reading has been written about it."[5]

Some, such as British professor of psychology Nicholas Humphrey, try to solve the problem by claiming that consciousness doesn't exist. Humphrey admits, though, that the question of consciousness does appear to pose a problem for science: "I think there *is* something remarkable going on. So remarkable that, as things stand, consciousness could still prove to be the Achilles heel of Darwinism, or (if I may switch metaphors) the smoking gun that gives the champions of Intelligent Design the evidence they seek that human beings did not evolve entirely by natural selection." (emphasis in the original)

Then he switches gears and explains why consciousness is *not* a problem for Darwinists:

Nonetheless, even though we should not try to explain it away, this doesn't mean we must assume that consciousness is *not* an illusion. Our starting assumption as scientists ought to be that on some level consciousness has to be an illusion. The reason is obvious. If nothing in the physical world can have the features that consciousness seems to have, then consciousness cannot exist as a thing in the physical world. So, while we should concede that as conscious subjects we do indeed have a valid experience of there being something in our minds that the rules of the physical universe don't apply to, this has to be *all it is* – the *experience of something in our minds.*[6] [emphasis in the original]

To some, Humphrey's proposition raises more questions than it answers. First, why should "our starting assumption as scientists ... be that on some level consciousness has to be an illusion"? Why should scientists start by assuming *anything* about consciousness? Science is the attempt to discover and understand reality. Preconceived notions seem contrary to that pursuit. Rather, starting out with a bias is not science but the attempt to defend a preset worldview, in this case the materialistic idea that matter is all there is.

The crux of Humphrey's argument rests in the sentence "If nothing in the physical world can have the features that consciousness seems to have, then consciousness cannot exist as a thing in the physical world." Here Humphrey seems to take it for granted that physical nature constitutes the totality of reality, so that in this world nothing outside the physical can exist. But that simply begs the question and doesn't add anything to our understanding of consciousness. He is discussing the *nature* of reality, and no one in science has yet established that physical nature constitutes reality in toto or that everything in nature follows the laws of physics. Humphrey has simply given us his own worldview – and the worldview of the philosophical materialists.

> **We must either revise our conception of consciousness or revise our conception of nature.**

But for science to understand the nature of reality scientists must ask, Is there more to reality than the physical? Although Humphrey may not have asked this question, others have. The Australian philosopher of mind David Chalmers disagrees with philosophical materialism when he says that consciousness is nonphysical and that to consider it nonexistent goes against all common sense. How can consciousness, which everyone experiences and which is the foundation of all other experiences and knowledge, simply not exist? In his paper *Consciousness and Its Place in Nature,* Chalmers writes, "[O]n the most common conception of consciousness, it is not easy to see how it could be part of the physical world. So it seems that to find a place for consciousness within the natural order, we must either revise our conception of consciousness or revise our conception of nature."[7]

Chalmers adds, "[To] deny without argument that there is a hard problem of consciousness over and above the easy problems would be to make a highly counterintuitive claim that begs the important questions."

The physicist and Nobel laureate Eugene Wigner (1902–1995) also disagreed with Humphrey: "There are two kinds of reality or existence: the existence of my consciousness and the reality or existence of everything else.... The latter reality is not absolute but only relative."[8]

Wigner reasoned that external, measurable phenomena, including matter, were known to him only through his consciousness, which must therefore, if anything, be more real than the phenomena. The British physicist Sir Arthur Eddington (1882–1944) thought similarly: "In comparing the certainty of things spiritual and things temporal, let us not forget this: mind is the first and most direct thing in our experience; all else is inference."[9] And "The only subject presented to me for study is the content of my consciousness."[10]

To account for consciousness without contradicting the known laws of physics, one approach has been to consider it an "epiphenomenon," an incidental effect of neural processes but not a cause of them. This idea was first proposed by Thomas Huxley, Darwin's contemporary and ally. At first Huxley admitted the seemingly irreducible nature of consciousness:

> I understand the main tenet of materialism to be that there is nothing in the universe but matter and force; and that all the phenomena of nature are explicable by deduction from the properties assignable to these two primitive factors.... It seems to me pretty plain that there is a third thing in the universe, to wit, consciousness, which ... I cannot see to be matter or force, or any conceivable modification of either.[11]

Thomas Huxley

But then Huxley proposed the idea of consciousness as an epiphenomenon. Physical (neurological and chemical) processes in the brain, he suggested, cause mental processes, but those mental processes, symptomatic of consciousness, have no causal role in the physical ones. Huxley compared mental events to a steam whistle that contributes nothing to the work of a locomotive.

This idea raises more problems than it solves. First, neither Huxley nor any other proponent of epiphenomenonalism has specified a mechanism by which consciousness could arise from physical processes. Second, we have to consider this viewpoint's really awkward notion that consciousness cannot act on the system of matter from which it has arisen – the neural impulses, the sensory organs, the brain itself. In physics, all aspects of a physical system have at least some effect on the behavior of the total system. Why should consciousness be an exception? Are the ephiphenomenalists suggesting that consciousness functions outside the laws of nature?

Another school of thought is panpsychism. This is an ancient philosophy, though over the centuries it has come to have various names and a number of subbranches. Among the philosophers who espoused panpsychism was Baruch Spinoza (1632–1677). Spinoza believed in one universal substance, each part of which has both physical and psychic properties. According to this view, even an atom would have some dim atomic awareness, and as more complex organizations of matter develop, correspondingly more complex forms of consciousness would emerge.

Panpsychism, which attributes some degree of consciousness to even disorganized matter, provides a possible evolutionary explanation for the appearance of consciousness. The German zoologist Bernhard Rensch (1900–1990), a proponent of this approach, posited, in addition to the physical properties of matter, what he calls "parallel psychic components," such as consciousness. "Molecules and atoms should also be credited with basic parallel components of some kind," he stated. "These parallel processes can be recognized as such only after the respective molecules have become part of the psychophysical substance (nerve and sense cells) of an organism, so that the parallel components form a complex of conscious phenomena that can be 'experienced.'"[12]

One difficulty with this approach involves the unity of consciousness. If every atom is separately conscious, then what mechanism integrates their awareness? Why should a carbon atom think or feel any different in a human brain than in a piece of wood? And since the brain is merely a combination of various atoms, why is the brain's consciousness unified and not just a mere sum total of all these atomic consciousnesses? This difficulty was recognized by the neurobiologist John C. Eccles, also a Nobel laureate, who wrote, "Hitherto it has been impossible to develop any neurophysiological theory that explains how a diversity of brain events comes to be synthesized so that there is a unified conscious experience of a global or gestalt character. The brain events remain disparate, being essentially the individual actions of countless neurons that are built into complex circuits."[13]

If patterns of matter also have consciousness and we are merely one set of these patterns, then two conclusions follow. First, there must exist complex metaphysical laws governing the production of consciousness in response to the presence of certain patterns. Second, in comparison with the individual consciousness of each element of the pattern, the consciousness of the pattern itself must be an entirely new metaphysical entity, a "higher" consciousness capable of accounting for our unified human experience. At this point we would have within the human body a rather complicated metaphysical apparatus consisting of varieties of conscious entities (trillions of semiconscious atoms, patterns possessing higher unifying consciousness) and laws governing their appearance. All this seems to raise more problems than it solves.

Perhaps a more straightforward solution to the problem of consciousness would be to revive the concept of the soul – a single irreducible unit of consciousness capable of functioning as the integrator of experience within the body. By soul we mean, by definition, a nonmaterial entity inhabiting a material body. In light of what we have discussed so far, at least the possibility of the soul's existence is worthy of serious consideration, since the soul provides a direct solution to the question of what consciousness actually is, and, in comparison to other possibilities, as discussed above, appears to be the most simple and direct explanation for the phenomenon of consciousness. Furthermore, the soul's existence – or at least the presence of something nonmaterial in all living beings – is supported by a wide variety of empirical evidence, especially in studies dealing with near-death experiences (NDEs) and reincarnation.

Near-death Experiences

In 1991, thirty-five-year-old American singer and songwriter Pam Reynolds was diagnosed with a basilar artery aneurysm – a severely swollen blood vessel in the brain stem. She was told that sooner or later the aneurysm would burst and therefore she could die at any moment. To attempt to drain the aneurysm was too risky and would probably kill her. Her only chance of survival was a rare and dangerous operation involving hypothermic cardiac arrest: her body would be cooled to the temperature of clinical death and her heart and breathing stopped. At that point the swollen artery would soften, and the aneurysm could be excised with much less risk. Afterwards, her body would be warmed to her normal temperature, and, if all went well, she would be revived.

Reynolds consented to the operation. Her breathing and heartbeat were stopped, and the blood was drained from her head, effectively stopping her brain waves. Her temperature was reduced to 15 degrees Celsius. The surgeons then opened her skull, removed the aneurysm, and reversed all the other procedures. Pam was then successfully revived and she returned to normal consciousness.

When she awoke, Pam told her doctors that she had been conscious during the operation and had observed everything from a space above her body. She went on to relate details of the operation, describing the saw the doctors had used to open her skull and how the nurse had shaved only a portion of her hair. She also correctly repeated what a nurse had said: "We have a problem. Her arteries are too small."

Pam's experience sounds like hundreds of other reported near-death experiences (NDEs), but her case is particularly striking because throughout the operation her brain was carefully monitored and the monitors showed no brain or brain stem activity. Pam Reynolds had one of the best-documented NDEs to date.[14]

Throughout history and in cultures throughout the world, people have reported near-death experiences in which, often while in a coma or unconscious state, they experience leaving their body and observing it and other aspects of the world from a position outside the body. Sometimes these people observe someone else trying to resuscitate them, and sometimes they report leaving the immediate vicinity of the body and traveling to places where they have encounters with divine

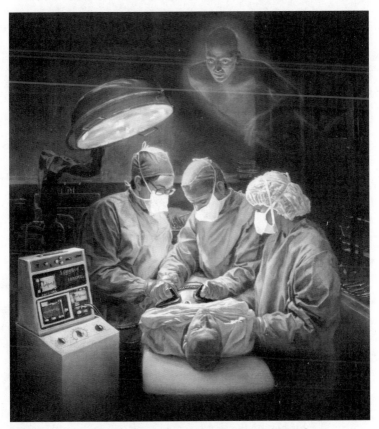

People who clinically should have been unconscious have observed events from a perspective outside their bodies and reported details that later were verified.

beings or deceased relatives. Most speak about being sucked back into the body.

Since the 1970s several scientists have completed serious studies on NDEs. One of these scientists is the American cardiologist Michael B. Sabom. After years of coming in almost daily contact with people resuscitated from clinical death, although skeptical, he decided to systematically study the near-death experience, especially by interviewing patients. He did not inform his subjects about his interest in near-death experiences, but only asked them to tell him what they could remember just before they lost consciousness. They were then asked if they remembered anything after falling unconscious. Some of the patients remembered nothing, but others asked him why he wanted to know. Sabom would then go on to explain that some patients had conscious experiences while they were apparently unconscious and as a scientist he was interested in learning more about the phenomenon. Most patients related their case with words like "You won't believe this, but ..."[15]

During his research, Sabom met, for example, a fifty-seven-year-old construction worker who told of hovering a meter and a half above his own body when it was on the operating table. The man proceeded to describe in detail how the doctors and nurses had conducted the operation.[16] In another case a soldier who had been fighting in Vietnam told how he had been flown, unconscious, away from the battlefield and had then observed the operation doctors had performed on him at a nearby hospital. At one point, he said, he experienced leaving the site of the operation and returning to the battlefield, where he saw soldiers collecting bodies in body bags. He tried to contact the soldiers, he said, but found himself unable. Then he suddenly found himself back in the hospital, where he re-entered his body.[17]

As I've mentioned, some of Sabom's patients gave specific details about their operations. Sabom was doubtful about these narrations, and as a seasoned cardiologist with almost one hundred heart operations under his belt he thought he could easily refute them. However, one of the subjects caused him to change his mind. This was a fifty-two-year-old night watchman who had undergone two heart surgeries. The watchman told Sabom about an NDE that had occurred during his first operation. Then, after some hesitation, he went on to describe a second NDE during the second operation. He described to Sabom in depth his operation, with details later confirmed by comparison to the surgical record. He even mentioned details the surgeon had not recorded but later confirmed true. The patient had no access to the surgeon's report.[18]

A total of thirty-two patients told Sabom about their NDEs, and Sabom also interviewed a control group of twenty-five cardiac patients who had undergone similar operations without experiencing NDEs. Two of these twenty-five could say nothing about their surgeries, twenty described something but made significant errors in their descriptions, and three gave correct but generalized and limited descriptions. On the other hand, out of the thirty-two patients who had experienced an NDE, twenty-six gave general descriptions of their operations without errors, and six related amazingly accurate details, confirmed by medical reports.[19]

The Dutch cardiologist Pim van Lommel has also investigated NDEs. Between 1988 and 2004 he interviewed 344 heart-attack survivors, all within a week of resuscitation from clinical death. When people are clinically dead, we would expect them to be beyond experience, but sixty-two of these survivors, or 18 percent, reported memories during the period when they were clinically dead. And 7 percent had "very deep" NDEs. In similar British and American studies in 2001 and 2003, the rates for deep experiences were 6.3 percent and 10 percent respectively.[20]

Van Lommel tells the story of a nurse who removed the dentures from a forty-five-year-old heart-attack victim during his resuscitation and placed them in a drawer in the crash cart. The patient was successfully revived from his unconscious state. A week later the same nurse saw him again on the hospital ward. She reported, "The moment he sees me he says, 'Oh, that nurse knows where my dentures are.' I am very surprised. Then he elucidates: 'You were there when I was brought into the hospital, and you took my dentures out of my mouth and put them onto that cart. It had all these bottles on it and there was this sliding drawer underneath, and that's where you put my teeth.' I was especially amazed because I remembered this happening while the man was in deep coma and in the process of CPR."[21]

Sabom writes, "Could the mind which splits apart from the physical brain be, in essence, the soul, which continues to exist after final bodily death, according to some religious doctrines? As I see it, this is the ultimate question that has been raised by reports of NDE."[22]

Children Remembering Previous Lives

Reincarnation refers to the idea that some aspect of personal identity survives the death of the body and is reborn into a new body and a new life. Let's look at what are probably the most extensive scientific studies of reincarnation so far performed. These studies were undertaken by the Canadian psychiatrist Ian Stevenson (1918–2007), who served as head of the Division of Personality Studies at the University of Virginia in Charlottesville, USA. Stevenson spent forty-five years investigating cases of small children who apparently remembered previous lives. In almost 3,000 cases he was able to confirm the existence of a deceased person who corresponded with a particular child's memories. Dr. Stevenson wrote,

Children who claim to remember previous lives have been found in every part of the world where they have been looked for … but they are found most easily in the countries of South Asia. Typically, such a child begins to speak about a previous life almost as soon as it can speak, usually between the ages of two and three; and typically it stops doing so between the ages of five and seven … Although some of the children make only vague statements, others give details of names and events that permit identifying a person whose life and death corresponds to the child's statements. In some instances the person identified is already known to the child's family, but in many cases this is not so. In addition to making verifiable statements about a deceased person, many of the children show behavior (such as a phobia) that is unusual in their family but found to correspond to behavior shown by the deceased person concerned or conjecturable for him.[23]

Ian Stevenson wrote mainly for the scientific community and published numerous papers on his research in technical journals. His first book, *Twenty Cases Suggestive of Reincarnation*, published in 1966, detailed his investigation into seven cases from India, three from Sri Lanka, two from Brazil, seven from the Tlingit Indians in Alaska, and one from Lebanon. Over the next thirty years Stevenson wrote several more books on the topic of reincarnation, culminating in 1997 in a book of more than 2200 pages titled *Reincarnation and Biology: A Contribution to the Etiology of Birthmarks and Birth Defects*. In this book he detailed 225 cases in which children who seemed to remember a previous life had birthmarks or birth defects that corresponded to features from the life of the "previous personality." A 200-page abbreviation of this work, *Where Reincarnation and Biology Intersect*, was published that same year for a lay audience.

Dr. Stevenson began his research in 1960 when he heard about a case in Sri Lanka. He interviewed the child and his parents as well as the people who had supposedly been the child's parents during the previous life. This was a research method he would use for all his later cases. In each case, he methodically documented the child's statements. Then he attempted to identify a deceased person who matched the child's description of a former identity, family, residence, and manner of death. Stevenson made every effort to find out whether the child's statements could have had their origin in normally acquired information – for example, whether the child had seen on television any details of the birthplace of the supposed previous personality or heard about a deceased family member through relatives. When possible, of course, Stevenson tried to reach the child before he or she was able to speak to the previous personality's family. Also whenever possible, he compared birthmarks and defects on the child's body with medical reports of wounds or scars on the deceased. He also studied otherwise unexplained features, habits, or behaviors in the child that were typical of the previous personality.

Ian Stevenson's subjects were all everyday people. *Washington Post* journalist Tom Shroder followed Stevenson on a field trip to India and described his subjects like this:

> The evidence he is referring to does not come from fashionable New Age sources, past-life readings, or hypnotic regressions. It is homely and specific: A boy remembers being a twenty-five-year-old mechanic thrown to his death from a speeding car on a beach road. He recalls the name of the driver, the exact location of the crash, the names of the mechanic's sisters and parents and cousins, and the people he hunted with.
>
> A girl remembers being a teenager named Sheila who was killed while crossing the road. She names the town Sheila lived in, plus Sheila's parents and siblings. When Sheila's family hears of the little girl's stories, they visit with her – in front of witnesses who say the girl recognized them by name and relationship without prompting.
>
> From the time he learns to talk, a boy in Virginia named Joseph calls his mother by her name and calls his grandmother Mom. As he grows, Joseph begins recalling obscure events from the life of his Uncle David, who died in an accident twenty years before Joseph was born – and who has been rarely mentioned because of the family's abiding grief.[24]

Another case is that of Sukla Gupta, who was born in 1954 as the daughter of a Bengali railroad worker. When she was small she would wrap a wooden block in cloth and cradle it in her arms, calling it Minu. She said that Minu was her daughter, and she also talked about Minu's father and two brothers. According to Sukla they lived in a village named Bhatpara, some distance from where she was born. When she was four years old she insisted on being taken there. Her father made some investigations and found out that a woman named Mana had lived in Bhatpara and died a few years earlier, indeed leaving behind an infant daughter named Minu. He brought Sukla to Bhatpara, where, on her own, she found the house where Mana had once lived. Out of more than thirty people who should have been unknown to her, Sukla pointed out Mana's husband, mother-in-law, and brother-in-law, and Minu.[25]

Ian Stevenson considered the evidence most strongly suggestive of reincarnation in cases where birthmarks or

Sukla, the daughter of a Bengali railway worker, who knew of many details in the life of a woman named Mana who died before Sukla was born.

defects on the child's body seemed to correspond to events in the life of a previous personality, especially if postmortem or other medical records for the previous personality were available. Hanumant Saxena was one such case. Hanumant was born in 1955 in the Farrukhabad District in Uttar Pradesh, India. He was born with a number of birthmarks along the lower midline of his chest. At three years old he began to speak about his previous life as Maha Ram, a farmer of the same village, who had died of shotgun wounds to the lower midline of his chest a year before Hanumant was born. As a small child Hanumant told his parents he had been shot in the location of his birthmarks, and he made other statements about Maha Ram's life that turned out to be correct. When Stevenson looked at the postmortem report on Maha Ram, he saw that the pattern of Maha Ram's wounds corresponded almost exactly to the birthmarks on Hanumant's chest.[26]

David Ray Griffin, an American professor of philosophy of religion and theology, lists the reasons he considers the results of Stevenson's research authentic:

The reports come spontaneously from small children, who usually lose these memories as they grow older.

There is generally only a short time between the birth of the child and the death of the previous personality. Manufactured cases usually go further back in time, often centuries.

The remembered person usually comes from the same culture and geographical area. In false cases this is not so.

Statements about the past life that can be verified turn out to be 80 or 90 percent correct.

Persons other than the child's parents testify to the child's statements and the behaviors related to the previous personality.

Neither the reporting children nor their relatives have anything to gain from the memories in terms of money or status. In fact, many of the cases are unpleasant experiences for everyone involved, including the child.

Memories of past lives are sometimes corroborated by behavioral patterns, talents and abilities, languages, and birthmarks or birth defects that can be associated with the previous personality.[27]

Explanations other than reincarnation have been advanced to account for these children's memories. For example, perhaps these children had exceptional paranormal abilities and could obtain undisclosed information about a deceased person by reading other people's minds. Stevenson pointed out, however, that none of the children he interviewed showed any particular paranormal ability. This proposal also does not explain the corresponding birthmarks and birth defects associated with some of the cases.

Another possibility is that the children were possessed by a discarnate personality. Of course, in cases where the children had birthmarks corresponding to features of the previous personality and expressed their identification with that personality as soon as they could, the discarnate personality would have had to possess the child in embryo. Entertaining this possibility, Stevenson wondered in what respect it would differ from reincarnation.

It has also been proposed that the children might have gathered their information not from memories of a previous life but from a shared spiritual region of information and experience with which the children lost contact as they grew up. But this again does not explain the cases involving birthmarks or explain why a child would so strongly identify with only one person.

Stevenson concluded: "I think a rational person, if he wants, can believe in reincarnation on the basis of evidence."[28]

About the greater implications of his research he wrote: "It has been wisely said that the question of a life after death is the most important one that a scientist – or anyone – can ask.... I am well aware that the fear of death may encourage a belief in a life after death. It is true that many of us want to believe in a life after death, but our wish that something may be true does not make it false. We may, after all, be engaged in a dual evolution – of our bodies and of our minds or souls."[29]

Souls in All Living Bodies?

The evidence presented in this chapter, I believe, suggests that a person can rationally accept consciousness as the symptom of a nonmaterial soul inhabiting the human body. Could such a nonmaterial soul also dwell in all life forms? Could the body of a tree or ant or fish also be only a temporary housing for a nonphysical spark of consciousness, a soul?

If we study nature, we will inevitably see that each life form exhibits at least some level of intelligence, even if only enough to protect itself from harm and keep itself fed. This intelligence appears symptomatic of consciousness, which in turn suggests a nonphysical presence inhabiting the body. So it would seem that a simple explanation of life is that living bodies of all types serve as vehicles through which particles of nonmaterial consciousness – selves – express themselves.

CHAPTER 12

The Scientific Aspect
of the Supernatural

I n this chapter we will take a better look at what scientists call the
paranormal, psi phenomena, or, often pejoratively, the supernatural. These words are variously used to refer to observable, nonphysical phenomena that appear to violate the known laws of physics.
The phenomena are often associated with the power of the mind and
consciousness in humans and sometimes animals.

The laws of physics deal with such principles as the laws governing gravity, motion, electromagnetism, and the strong and weak forces
inside atoms. An event falls into the category of "paranormal" when
such laws cannot explain the event.

The previous chapter discussed, in some depth, indicators of a nonmaterial consciousness in human beings, as shown through NDEs and
studies on reincarnation. It turns out that such studies show only a
small sample of the range of paranormal phenomena and how widely
these phenomena are accepted.[1]

What should we make of the paranormal? Of course, committed
materialists – and nowadays most scientists would include themselves

in this category – tend to simply brush it away, considering it the stuff of superstition, something not to be taken seriously. But let's step back from such skepticism and give the phenomena consideration, if for no other reason than that reports of it are so widespread. And a principle of science is that things deserve to be studied with an open mind and the evidence examined without bias.

The reason I have included in this book a discussion on the paranormal is obvious: Modern evolutionary thinking typically tries to reduce everything to matter and explain away indications for anything non-physical or beyond material nature. By demonstrating the shortcomings of this mode of thinking, intelligent design points to something apart from matter. If evidence for the paranormal can be substantiated, this can only strengthen the case that intelligent design proponents seek to make.

I also feel justified in including this discussion in a book on science because a large body of scientific evidence supporting the existence of the paranormal has been gathered over the last century and a half by mainstream scientists, among them some of the most famous of all time – such luminaries as Marie and Pierre Curie and Alfred Russel Wallace, the co-founder of the theory of evolution.

This research into the paranormal challenges the belief that everything in nature (and within living organisms) can be reduced to matter. Thus it strengthens the case for the existence of a nonmaterial consciousness – something most people call the soul – and suggests that the human mind (or any entity's mind) can affect matter in ways beyond the known laws of physics. For example, it seems that persons with sufficient mental concentration can communicate with others without contacting them verbally or through other normal means (the ability known as telepathy) and can move matter without physically touching it (an ability known as telekinesis).

The Psi Effect

In 1989 the mainstream scientific journal *Foundations of Physics* published a study done by physicist Dean Radin and psychologist Roger

Nelson, both from Princeton University, on 597 experiments conducted between 1959 to 1987. In these experiments, test subjects were asked to mentally influence random number generators (RNGs) – electronic machines that randomly generate zeros and ones – so that the machines would churn out more ones than zeros or vice versa. Normally, with a sufficiently large number of trials, the distribution of ones and zeros should be equal. However, Radin and Nelson found in these 597 experiments a distribution of 51%–49% instead of the normal 50%–50%. That doesn't sound like much of a difference, but the probability that this would happen by sheer chance is less than 10^{-12} (1 out of one trillion).[2]

In March 2004 *New Scientist's* cover story "Power of the Paranormal: Why It Won't Surrender to Science" again discussed the stubborn problem that scientists were now calling the psi effect. Further studies had only confirmed what Radin and Nelson had concluded in 1989. In 2007 Radin wrote, "There are disagreements over how to interpret the evidence, but the fact is that virtually all scientists who have studied the evidence, including the hard-nosed skeptics, now agree that something interesting is going on that merits serious scientific attention."[3]

Marie and Pierre Curie

Among the most famous scientists of all time are Marie Curie (1867–1934) and her husband Pierre (1859–1906), Nobel laureates and discoverers of radioactivity. Few people know that they were also among a number of prominent scientists who about a century ago conducted research into parapsychology. Pierre Curie wrote, "There is, according to me, a completely new domain of facts and physical states of space of which we presently have no idea."[4]

At the juncture of the nineteenth and twentieth centuries, systematic research into what are now often called psi phenomena was still in its infancy. Today modern researchers more often tend to investigate small-scale but statistically significant effects, like the influencing of the random-number generator. This allows for experimental repeatability and a high level of experimental control. But back then curious scientists more often investigated "special subjects" – that is, people who seemed endowed with exceptional paranormal abilities.

At this time, also, there was considerable public enthusiasm for what was called "spiritualism," the attempt to communicate with departed spirits through "mediums" or "sensitives," people who seemed to have psychic or paranormal powers. Certainly some, perhaps many, of these purported mediums were outright frauds. But amidst seemingly abundant chicanery was a residue of phenomena that seemed to deserve further scientific attention.

The Curies were among those scientists who gave such phenomena consideration and who attended and investigated spiritualist séances in Paris with the same scientific rigor they used to explore radioactivity. In a letter dated July 24, 1905, Pierre Curie wrote,

> We had at the Psychological Society a few séances with the medium Eusapia Paladino. It was very interesting, and truly those phenomena that we have witnessed seemed to us not to be some magical tricks – a table lifted four feet above the floor, movements of objects, feelings of hands that pinched you or caressed you, apparitions of light. All this in a room arranged by us, with a small number of spectators all well known and without the presence of a possible accomplice. Cheating would only be possible if the medium had extraordinary abilities as a magician. But how to explain the different phenomena when we are holding her hands and legs, and the lighting of the room is sufficient to see everything going on?[5]

Pierre Curie was killed in a road accident in 1906. His interest in spiritualism had continued up until his death. Marie Curie later remembered a talk between her husband and the mathematician Henri Poincaré the day before Pierre Curie died: "At one point, Eusapia was the subject of the conversation along with the phenomena she produces. Poincaré was objecting with a skeptical smile, curious of new things, while you

[Pierre] were pleading the reality of the phenomena. I was looking at your face while you were talking, and once more I was admiring your nice head, your charming words, enlightened by your smile. It was the last time that I was hearing you express your ideas."[6]

Alfred Russel Wallace

Another noteworthy scientist who became involved in paranormal research was Alfred Russel Wallace, coauthor of the theory of evolution. A few years after Darwin and Wallace introduced their theory to the world, their paths diverged. This was mainly because, while Darwin seemed to become more materialistic in outlook, Wallace began to study parapsychology and became one of the scientists most outspoken on the validity of paranormal experience. Indeed, Wallace's views so annoyed Darwin that Darwin once asked Wallace by letter if he were aware that he was "murdering our common child,"[7] or undermining the theory of evolution.

Wallace became interested in parapsychology as early as 1844, when experimenting with mesmerism. Mesmerism later developed into what became known as hypnotism, but Wallace's mesmerism appears to have also included induced phenomena of a more supernatural kind. For example, Wallace was studying the "community of sensation." He wrote, "The sympathy of sensation between my patient and myself was to me the most mysterious phenomenon I had ever witnessed. I found that when I laid hold of his hand, he felt, tasted, or smelled exactly the same as I did."[8]

Wallace went on to describe how he formed a chain of several persons. At one end he placed the mesmerized subject and at the other end himself. When someone pinched Wallace the subject would touch the corresponding part of his own body and complain of being pinched. If Wallace put a lump of sugar or a little salt in his mouth the subject would go through the motions of sucking and name the flavor Wallace was tasting.

In 1862, Wallace returned to England after many years in the tropics. He then began to research spiritualism and participate regularly in séances, and in 1866 wrote a treatise called "The Scientific Aspect of the Supernatural." There he listed about twenty of the most prominent intellectuals of his time who had all confirmed having personally witnessed paranormal phenomena.

Wallace also collaborated with Sir William Crookes (1832–1919), the celebrated English chemist and physicist, and President of the Royal Society, who on his own had researched spiritualism under controlled conditions. Together they investigated, among others, Daniel Dunglas Home, a medium with apparently extraordinary abilities. Wallace and Crookes would, unannounced, bring Home to places he had never been before. There he would demonstrate numerous spiritualistic phenomena, such as playing musical instruments without touching them and floating in the air and in and out of open windows. All of this took place in full daylight or in fully lit rooms before the eyes of Wallace and Crookes and other respected scientists.

Wallace wrote in 1896, "I ought to state that for twenty-five years I had been an utter skeptic as to the existence of any preterhuman or superhuman intelligences, and that I never for a moment contemplated the possibility that the marvels related by Spiritualists could be literally true. If I have now changed my opinion, it is simply by the force of evidence. It is from no dread of annihilation that I have gone into this subject; it is from no inordinate longing for eternal existence that I have come to believe in facts which render this highly probable, if they do not actually prove it."[9]

Wallace's involvement with spiritual phenomena not only dismayed Darwin but made quite a few other scientists see him as a renegade. Still, he was not deterred. He wrote, "I thus learned my first great lesson in the inquiry into these obscure fields of knowledge: never to accept the disbelief of great men, or their accusations of imposture or of imbecility, as of any great weight when opposed to the repeated observation of facts by other men admittedly sane and honest."[10]

As for his theory of evolution, Wallace continued to accept its premises throughout his life. But whereas mainstream Darwinists came to view evolution as an unguided material process, Wallace considered the evolution of species a divinely guided process meant to accommodate eternal spirits in physical bodies in an ongoing spiritual evolution.

Rupert Sheldrake and the Dog Jaytee

Among contemporary scientists investigating paranormal phenomena is the British biologist Dr. Rupert Sheldrake, perhaps one of the first scientists ever to test whether telepathy or other forms of mental communication can take place between animals and humans. In one experiment he tried to ascertain whether dogs are actually able to anticipate when their owner is returning home.[11]

Do dogs possess a sixth sense? Skeptics might insist that when a dog is aware that someone known to them is approaching, this must be due to the dog's normal keen senses of smell and hearing. Or perhaps the dog knows its master's routine. Or perhaps the dog responds to subtle cues from people around it, people who know the master's routine. Or perhaps those people simply notice the dog's behavior more when *they* are aware the master will soon return.

To test these and other possibilities, Sheldrake conducted a series of experiments using Pamela Smart and her dog Jaytee. Pamela and Jaytee lived in a ground-floor apartment in Ramsbottom, a suburb of Manchester, England. Pamela routinely left Jaytee with her retired parents, who lived next door. Her parents noticed that the dog seemed to anticipate Pamela's return. In 1991 Pamela was working as a secretary in Manchester, and every day Jaytee went to the French window in the living room around 4:30 P.M., the time when Pamela left work. Her journey home usually took 45 to 60 minutes. Jaytee would sit by the window through most of this time.

Pamela's parents ascribed Jaytee's behavior to Pamela's returning daily at the same time. However, in 1993 she became unemployed; she no longer left and returned according to a schedule but left at random times to go shopping or visit friends. Yet Jaytee still seemed to know when she was on her way home and would wait for her by the window.

In 1994 Pamela read a newspaper report of Sheldrake's research and contacted him, offering herself and Jaytee as subjects. The result was data from almost two hundred experiments conducted between May 1994 and July 1996 in which a video camera recorded events taking place at the window where Jaytee was accustomed to wait for Pamela. For her part, Pamela would record her whereabouts, the distance traveled, the mode of transport, and the time when she left to return home. At home her parents kept notes on Jaytee's behavior.

Five additional experiments took place with Jaytee at Pamela's sister's house in a nearby town, and fifty other experiments with Jaytee left alone in Pamela's flat. In all cases, Pamela herself turned on the video camera upon leaving and stopped it upon her return. Since the videotapes ran for only four hours, Pamela generally returned within a four-hour time frame, although she varied her time away between less than an hour and close to four hours. In ten control experiments, she returned after more than four hours.

How did Jaytee know Pamela was on her way home? He could not have heard her car approaching.

Pamela's absences took place at all times during the day, from early morning to late evening. In some of the experiments she chose her return time; in others Sheldrake would choose a random time and apprise her of it by beeper.

Two scientists who had not been told what the experiments were about examined the time-coded videos and independently recorded each of Jaytee's visits to the window. Their records were then compared with the notes Pamela had taken. As it turned out, whenever Pamela was not on her way home Jaytee spent 4 to 11 percent of his time at the window, often to bark at a passing cat or snooze in the sunshine. However, during the period when Pamela was on her way home Jaytee spent about 60 percent of his time at the window, most of the time, according to Pamela's parents, evidently anticipating her.

How did Jaytee know Pamela was on her way home? He could not have heard her car approaching, since in some cases he went to the window when she was still 50 kilometers away. Also, the heavy Greater Manchester traffic would have prevented him from singling out her car engine. Sometimes she left home without her car, taking instead a train or a taxi. Neither could he have picked up unconscious clues from Pamela's parents, since they were not informed when she would return. Pamela herself did not usually know her return time. And since Pamela left and returned randomly throughout the day, Jaytee could not have been responding to any daily routine.

In the ten control experiments where Pamela did not return within the four hours, at no point during those hours did Jaytee go to the window more than his usual 4 to 11 percent of the time. So although some might suspect that Jaytee's behavior simply indicated that the longer he was alone the more often he would approach the window to wait for his master, these ten experiments showed that not to be the case.

Sheldrake concludes: "Jaytee seemed to be detecting Pamela Smart's intention to come home in a way that could not be explained in terms of any of the 'normal' hypotheses considered above. Perhaps he was responding to her intentions or thoughts telepathically."[12]

How does telepathy work? Of course, we can't tell, but the mechanics of it seem unlikely to be physical – as through radio waves – since the brains neither of humans nor of dogs are known to emit or register radio waves. It may be that the mind possesses telepathic and other abilities to perceive and influence matter in subtle ways not currently understood by contemporary science. Another possibility, discussed in the next chapter, is that there is an all-pervading superior intelligence linking all beings and that under particular circumstances living beings can connect with this superior intelligence and access information they could not obtain by physical processes through their five senses. Perhaps telepathy and other such psychic abilities work through a combination of these two ways – through special capabilities of the mind and through linking with an all-pervading intelligence – or perhaps there is a third explanation.

Science Slanted for Public Consumption

One may wonder why, if telepathy and other parapsychological phenomena have been so well documented, they are not widely accepted by the mainstream scientific community. Perhaps many scientists refuse to consider the evidence because it challenges some of their widely held assumptions about reality.

In 2007 Channel 4, one of England's public television channels, contacted Rupert Sheldrake, requesting him to appear on their show "Enemies of Reason" with Richard Dawkins, professor of zoology at Oxford, well-known spokesperson for Darwinism and crusader for atheism. Rupert Sheldrake reports, "Soon before 'Enemies of Reason' was filmed, the production company, IWC Media, told me that Richard Dawkins wanted to visit me to discuss my research on unexplained abilities of people and animals. I was reluctant to take part, but the company's representative assured me that 'this documentary, at Channel 4's insistence, will be an entirely more balanced affair than 'The Root of All Evil?' was. ['The Root of All Evil?' was a program purporting to show that the root of the world's evils is religion.] She added, 'We are very keen for it to be a discussion between two scientists, about scientific modes of enquiry.' So I agreed and we fixed a date. I was still not sure what to expect ..."

Sheldrake related the discussion that, when the cameras came to film, actually took place. Dawkins, he said, dismissed the idea of telepathy out of hand, saying there was absolutely no evidence for telepathy or other parapsychological phenomena; people *want* to believe in parapsychology, but it's wishful thinking. Sheldrake continues:

We then agreed that controlled experiments were necessary. I said that this was why I had actually been doing such experiments, including tests to find out if people really could tell who was calling them on the telephone when the caller was selected at random. The results were far above the chance level.

The previous week I had sent Richard copies of some of my papers, published in peer-reviewed journals, so that he could look at the data. Richard seemed uneasy and said, "I don't want to discuss evidence."

"Why not?" I asked.

"There isn't time. It's too complicated. And that's not what this program is about." The camera stopped.

The Director, Russell Barnes, confirmed that he too was not interested in evidence. The film he was making was another Dawkins polemic.

I said to Russell, "If you're treating telepathy as an irrational belief, surely evidence about whether it exists or not is essential for the discussion. If telepathy occurs, it's not irrational to believe in it. I thought that's what we were going to talk about. I made it clear from the outset that I wasn't interested in taking part in another low-grade debunking exercise."

Richard said, "It's not a low-grade debunking exercise; it's a high-grade debunking exercise."

In that case, I replied, there had been a serious misunderstanding, because I had been led to believe that this was to be a balanced scientific discussion about evidence. Russell Barnes asked to see the emails I had received from his assistant. He read them with obvious dismay, and said the assurances she had given me were wrong. The team packed up and left.[13]

Thoughts on Claims of Fraud Surrounding the Paranormal

At this point it seems essential to discuss fraud and the exposure of fraud that surrounds research into the paranormal.

First a general scientific principle: Scientific inquiry requires unbiased skepticism. For example, it would be wrong for a scientist to be skeptical of evidence that goes against a favored theory and remain open only to evidence that supports it.

Second: If there have been confirmed instances of fraud among those claiming to possess paranormal powers, or those who have investigated them (and indeed there have been), this hardly justifies dismissing the entire study of reported paranormal phenomena. If whenever we find instances of fraud in a given field we are to throw out all the evidence from that field, then *every* branch of science would have to be dismissed, because virtually all of them have confirmed instances of fraud.

It may be that even some of the most celebrated scientists of the past who have investigated allegedly paranormal phenomena have sometimes been hoodwinked. Nonetheless, their willingness to investigate the phenomena typifies the true spirit of scientific inquiry.

As it turns out, today's professional journals in paranormal research typically apply unusually high standards to guard against fraud. In *Betrayers of the Truth,* written in 1983, William Broad and Nicholas Wade fill a book with cases of fraud found in scientific fields such as astronomy, biology, chemistry, geology, medical research, and in one instance, parapsychology. The authors comment, "Because parapsychology is still regarded as a fringe subject not properly part of science, its practitioners have striven to be more than usually rigorous in following correct scientific methodology."[14]

Thus we find in parapsychology rigorous experiments performed and replicated. Indeed, we find the sort of research protocols expected for scientific work of the very highest quality. I believe, therefore, that evidence from paranormal research deserves serious consideration. A number of prominent contemporary scientists, some of them among the most reputed of our time, seem to agree.

A New Physics and Understanding of Reality?

"The question of whether paranormal phenomena actually exist probably divides educated members of modern Western civilization as sharply as any other single issue. If it is true that the human brain can receive messages and control things in ways that cannot be explained normally, then this undermines the belief of most scientists and runs contrary to the belief of most of us who actually investigate the brain."[15]

These were the opening remarks of physiologist Horace Barlow at an unusual interdisciplinary conference in Cambridge in April 2000 titled "Rational Perspectives on the Paranormal," attended by about fifty physicists, psychiatrists, and psychologists, some skeptical about the paranormal, others more open to accepting its reality. Among the latter was Fotini Pallikari, a physicist from the University of Athens.

Pallikari presented data from a group of psychologists who had investigated whether people could influence the proportion of randomly generated ones and zeros. The data was analyzed by two different statistical methods. One of the methods detected no significant difference between the results of the "uninfluenced" tests and the tests in which the subjects tried to exert an influence. But the second analysis showed a weak effect in favor of the subjects' being able to influence the outcome. These and other such experiments failed to convince the skeptics, but I mention it because it shows that research into parapsychology continues to attract prominent scientists.

One such scientist is the world-renowned British physicist and Nobel laureate Brian Josephson, who in 1962 at the age of twenty-two, discovered what is now known in quantum physics as the Josephson effect. Around 1970 his interest shifted from pure physics to studying how the brain works. At the same time, he also became interested in Eastern mysticism and parapsychology. At one point he attended a conference at which a psychic demonstrated spoon-bending. "I began to sense that conventional science is inadequate for situations where the mind is involved, and the task of clarification became a major concern of mine," Josephson relates.[16]

According to Josephson, there is now strong evidence for the existence of parapsychological phenomena. He maintains that phenomena such as telepathy, telekinesis, and remote viewing are scientifically demonstrable and that scientists have to start seriously considering whether present ideas of physics are inadequate:

Science needs to try to understand the observer, and to respond vigorously to 'the challenge of consciousness research.' Physics ... may have moved too fast toward a tempting conclusion [that the laws of quantum physics are the ultimate description of reality] and thrown out the crucial and subtle intelligence of the observer as a part of this process. [17]

Josephson has also stated that mind and consciousness may have a reality independent of matter, a notion which may ultimately change the way science looks at the world:

> What are the implications for science of the fact that psychic functioning appears to be a real effect? These phenomena seem mysterious, but no more mysterious perhaps than strange phenomena of the past which science has now happily incorporated within its scope. What ideas might be relevant in the context of suitably extending science to take these phenomena into account? Two such concepts are those of the observer, and non-locality. The observer forces his way into modern science because the equations of quantum physics, if taken literally, imply a universe that is constantly splitting into separate branches, only one of which corresponds to our perceived reality. A process of "decoherence" has been invoked to stop two branches interfering with each other, but this still does not answer the question of why our experience is of one particular branch and not any other. Perhaps, despite the unpopularity of the idea, the experiencers of the reality are also the selectors.[18]

So the universe may, as Josephson suggests, have been selected by us conscious observers and not merely perceived. At this we may ask, *Which* conscious observers? You? Me? Everyone else? The next chapter will take a further look at evidence suggesting that indeed behind all of nature lies one conscious observer, an observer with capabilities that far exceed those of the conscious observers within our ordinary experience.

CHAPTER 13

Inspiration, Instinct, and Superconsciousness

One puzzling mental phenomenon is inspiration, the state in which ideas difficult or even impossible to conceive through normal thought processes enter the mind fully formed, as if from an external source. Inspiration plays a central role in all creative human endeavors. Wolfgang Amadeus Mozart (1756–1791) once described his creative process like this:

> When I feel well and in good humor, or when I am taking a drive or walk … thoughts crowd into my mind as easily as you could wish. Whence and how do they come? I do not know and have nothing to do with it…. Once I have a theme, another melody comes, linking itself with the first one, in accordance with the needs of the composition as a whole. It does not come to me successively, with its various parts worked

Wolfgang Amadeus Mozart

out in detail, as they will be later on, but it is in its entirety that my imagination lets me hear it.[1]

Aside from inspiration in the arts, the phenomenon plays a central role in solving difficult scientific and mathematical problems as well. The problems investigators can successfully tackle by mental endeavor alone are usually only routine; significant advances in science almost always involve sudden inspirations, which in many instances come unexpectedly after a lull in a long period of intense but unsuccessful problem-solving.

An incident from the life of the mathematician Karl Gauss (1777–1855) shows a typical example of this phenomenon. After trying unsuccessfully for years to prove a certain theorem about whole numbers, he suddenly grasped the solution. He described his experience: "Finally, two days ago I succeeded.... Like a sudden flash of lightning the riddle happened to be solved. I myself cannot say what was the conducting thread which connected what I previously knew with what made my success possible."[2]

Inspiration would thus seem to come from a source external to the conscious subject and provide information not obtained by conscious effort. The French mathematician Henri Poincaré (1854–1912), after deeply considering the phenomenon of inspiration in his own work, was led to contemplate a source that resembled a sort of divine intervention. Poincaré called this source "the subliminal self" and described it as follows: "[It is] in no way inferior to the conscious self; it is not purely automatic; it is capable of discernment; it has tact, delicacy; it knows how to choose, to divine. What can I say? It knows better how to divine than the conscious self, since it succeeds where that has failed. In a word, is not the subliminal self superior to the conscious self?"[3]

Instincts: Inspiration in Nature?

Intelligence, knowledge, and inspiration from a source beyond the reach of normal consciousness could be widespread not only among humans but throughout the living world. In *Nature's IQ*, a book published in

2009 by Hornyánszky Balázs and Tasi István, two Hungarian scientists, the authors give numerous examples of behavioral patterns in nature that could suggest a superior guiding intelligence.

What, for example, makes ants and bees create exquisite symbiotic communities, in which each individual works selflessly in a coordinated effort for the sake of the whole? Human organizations – large corporations, for example – also rely on symbiotic cooperation, but in such organizations the cooperation is aided by a manager or director. Among bees and ants there appear to be no managers, yet bees and ants act in harmony for the overall good of their societies far better than humans cooperate in any known human organization. Is this due to genetic preprogramming, or is something more going on?

Another striking example of behavior that seems as though guided can be seen in migrating animals. The North American sockeye salmon (*Oncorhynchus nerka*) hatch in fresh-water rivers and springs but soon migrate to the sea, where they live for six years. At the end of those six years the salmon set out in early summer and return to the mouth of the very river from which they entered the sea. After gathering in schools for three or four days, the fish begin the almost impossible task of swimming against the river's current and back to their hatching grounds. With unbelievable energy, almost unstoppable, the fish struggle through meter-high sandbanks, over rocks, and, when they reach shallower waters, half-submerged tree trunks. The salmon fight their way through rapids and with the powerful strokes of their caudal fins climb waterfalls. Whenever the river or stream branches, they unfailingly choose the correct branch. Do they remember the route from six years earlier? That initial journey to the sea could have been as long as 2,000 kilometers. How do they know which way to go?

Some scientists say the salmon record in their memories the scent of the waters through which they pass on the way to the sea, and they retain these memories during their six years in the ocean. This is a surprising hypothesis because there is hardly any detectable chemical difference between one stream and another. Other scientists say "instinct," but one is left to wonder exactly what instinct is.[4]

And then there's the Arctic tern (*Sterna paradiseae*), a record-holder among migratory animals for distance traveled. Each year this medium-sized gull flies approximately 35,000 kilometers from the Arctic, where it nests, to the Antarctic, where it winters – and back.

Arctic terns hatch their eggs in the Arctic from May through November. It is common for a pair of Arctic terns to come back to nest in the same place each year. As winter approaches, terns from eastern Canada and Greenland cross the Atlantic Ocean, aided by the west winds, to join the European Arctic terns. Together these birds fly south along the western coasts of Europe and Africa. A small percentage stay in South Africa, and the rest fly to the islands around the Antarctic. The trip takes ninety days. Young terns do not return to the Arctic but travel counterclockwise around the Antarctic Circle for two or three years, spending their time somewhere along the shores of the Pacific Ocean. At maturity, in their third spring, they join the adults on the journey north toward their nesting sites in the Arctic.

Again, scientists call it instinct, and again, the word doesn't really answer the question.

Why do Arctic terns choose the earth's two farthest regions in which to live their lives? There are plenty of suitable lands in between. What pushes the terns to fly so far? Again, scientists call it instinct, and again the word doesn't really answer the question. Is such travel genetically preprogrammed, or does the same voice that inspired Mozart and Gauss whisper guidance in their ears?[5]

The ruby-throated hummingbird (*Archilochus colubris*), the only colibri species nesting in the eastern part of North America, weighs less than three grams, yet every year this bird braves the buffeting winds to fly across the Gulf of Mexico to spend its winters in Mexico and Central America – a distance away of almost 1000 kilometers. And the bird flies without stopping for food or rest. The flight takes twenty-five hours, and to keep aloft the bird flaps its wings seventy-five times per second, for a total of more than six million continuous wing strokes. According to the current understanding of metabolism, it seems the ruby-throated hummingbird shouldn't be able to make this journey; there is simply not enough room in its small body to store enough energy to complete the trip. Then scientists discovered that ruby-throated hummingbirds store surplus fat during the period preceding migration, roughly doubling their weight to six grams. And the birds take advantage of favorable tailwinds during the flight to accomplish the otherwise unlikely migration. But how does the hummingbird know when it is time to fatten itself up? How does it know how to take advantage of the favorable winds? And how did such a little bird get this impossible idea to migrate a thousand kilometers in the first place?[6]

Perhaps such birds have developed these behaviors after millions of years of evolution, and the adult birds teach whatever has not been encrypted in their genetic code to their hatchlings. But studies show that although animals do pass on their experiences to some degree, there appears to be more to it than that. For example, the cuckoo (*Cuculus canorus*) does not know its parents – cuckoo mothers lay their eggs in other birds' nests – but young cuckoos follow the same migration routes as their parents. No one has taught them where to go. Where does their knowledge come from if not from some external source of inspiration?[7]

An even more striking example is the monarch butterfly that lives in the northeastern part of North America. Within the course of the summer, three or four generations hatch and live their short lives in the American northeast. Then, in the fall, the butterflies of the fourth or fifth generation – millions of monarch butterflies – head south, fluttering as far as three thousand kilometers until they reach a small area in certain forests on Mexico's volcanic mountain peaks. There they live, lay their eggs, and die, and their descendants later migrate north.

Unlike the monarchs that make the journey south, all in one trip, the monarchs that begin the migration north go only part of the way. Their descendants in the next generation carry the journey further north, and only by the third or fourth generation do monarchs reach the final northern destinations to begin the whole sweeping cycle again.

Three to four generations live and die in the north between southern migrations. The butterflies that trek to Mexico are, twice over, the great-great-grandchildren of the last generation to have made it. And the butterflies that finally reach the American northeast on the migration north are, again twice over, the great-great-grandchildren of the last generation to have completed that trip.

National Geographic published a story about these butterflies in 2003, calling their migrations one of nature's greatest mysteries.[8] The butterflies certainly can't remember the way for a trip they have never made before. And they also cannot learn the way from other butterflies, since their forebears who last made the trip died generations ago. *National Geographic* would probably be the last publication to propose that a superior intelligence guides the butterflies, but is there a better explanation?

The Subliminal Self

As mentioned above, the mathematician Henri Poincaré was led by his own experience with inspiration to the idea of the "subliminal self," a self to which he ascribed almost supernatural properties ("Is not the subliminal self superior to the conscious self?"). Nevertheless, he backed away from the idea of *divine* inspiration: "I confess that for my part, I should hate to accept it."[9] He then offered a mechanical explanation of how the subliminal self, viewed as a machine, could account for inspiration. The subliminal self, Poincaré proposed, mechanically and randomly assembles numerous combinations of mathematical symbols until at last it finds a combination that satisfies the desire of the conscious mind to achieve a certain type of mathematical result.

Poincaré did not specify, however, how such a machine could have come into existence in the first place. Poincaré also knew well that the number of combinations involved in such a "brute-force" approach to problem-solving[10] could easily exceed the number of operations that the brain, over a short period of time, could reasonably be expected to perform. And Poincaré's proposed mechanism would not account for the creative energy going on in the brain of a Mozart or a Beethoven, because their compositions seemed to appear unexpectedly, like a gift, and were usually not solutions to any fixed problem.

As things stand, no one has proposed any testable theory or come up with even a reasonable suggestion as to how inspiration could arise from a physical mechanism. And although inspiration is a common experience, it remains a phenomenon to which science has given scant attention.

So what is the source of inspiration? One possibility is that it could originate in an all-pervading source of intelligence – a superconsciousness behind all phenomena.

The possible existence of an all-pervading superconsciousness has interesting implications for the theory of intelligent design, whose proponents have been discussing how involved such a background intelligence could be in nature's workings. Some propose what they call "front-loading" – the idea that the first living cell was created and intelligently programmed to evolve all other life forms without further intelligent involvement. Others propose a process of mainly natural evolution interrupted by occasional intelligent intervention. But a close look at what inspiration entails indicates that intelligent intervention may be a more ongoing part of nature.

CHAPTER 14

The Vedic Paradigm

The preceding chapter concluded the material I wanted to present. In this last chapter I will try to weave the various strands into a whole and address some of the issues raised. I will also explore what may be called an alternative paradigm, one derived from the philosophy of nature found in the Vedic texts of ancient India.

But so far I have presented material arguing that the Darwinian theory of evolution and the greater materialistic attempt to understand reality solely in terms of material laws have failed us. I have shown that the theory of evolution is beset with anomalies, holes, and contradictions: The speciation Darwin proposed has never been observed or demonstrated; modern biology has made the origin of life a bigger conundrum than Darwin ever imagined; today, as in Darwin's time, the fossil record is an embarrassment to the theory; and the evolutionary history of human origins is a colorful assortment of speculations.

In the cell's molecular machinery and what may be called the digital technology of the cell, whose genetic code functions analogously to modern computer code, we saw strong suggestions of intelligent design. After this, in chapter 10 we looked at certain features of the greater universe that also suggest intelligent design. In chapters 11, 12, and 13 I discussed evidence of the paranormal, evidence suggesting that consciousness is nonphysical and that mind can influence matter in ways not understandable by the laws of physics. I also introduced the inference that an ever-present intelligence of a higher nature may pervade and indeed interact with the natural world.

Having examined all this material, I for my part find it safe to conclude that Darwin is of the past. Yet for the last century and a half Darwinism has been, and still is, what historian of science Thomas Kuhn probably would have called the paradigm by which all evidence in the life sciences has been interpreted. So if, as I have proposed, Darwinism is a failed idea, then a new paradigm is needed to replace the role that Darwinism has played. In this chapter I conclude by exploring how well a paradigm derived from the Vedic literature can account for the anomalies that have accumulated under the reign of Darwinism.

I believe that a new paradigm is needed to explain the anomalies that Darwinism and its attendant materialistic worldview do not account for. It is needed to address issues like the inadequacy of natural causation, the evidence for intelligent design, and the fundamental nature of consciousness. It is needed to address the evidence for the presence of humans tens or even hundreds of millions of years ago. It is needed to explain the evidence for reincarnation and near-death experiences, and it is needed to help us better understand the phenomena of inspiration and instinct. A Vedic paradigm accounts for these, and it also consistently addresses the concealed theological argumentation that Darwin and his followers have employed in their scientific reasoning ever since the theory was first presented.

The Role and Nature of Paradigms

Paradigm has become a fashionable word and been given various shades of meaning. But when applied to the philosophy of science it has a particular definition. Thomas Kuhn himself introduced the term in this context in 1962 in his landmark book *The Structure of Scientific Revolutions,* where he pointed out the crucial role paradigms play in all scientific endeavors.

The Merriam-Webster dictionary now defines *paradigm* in scientific usage as "a philosophical and theoretical framework of a scientific school or discipline within which theories, laws, and generalizations, and the experiments performed in support of them, are formulated; broadly: a philosophical or theoretical framework of any kind."

Simply put, scientific paradigms are conceptual models of reality scientists use to make sense of their evidence. A paradigm is like a map. A map is not a place or even a route to a place; rather, it is a chart that shows enough features of the routes and surrounding areas to help us see where we are and get where we want to go. We all have maps – paradigms – which we use to make sense of the world; we couldn't function without them.

Kuhn wrote that paradigms enable scientists to make wonderful discoveries because paradigms provide a framework within which to fit bits of evidence together, like pieces of a puzzle, to form a larger picture; as scientists assemble the evidence, they can see what pieces are missing and direct their research in that direction. In this way, paradigms greatly help science push forward.

But when paradigms are inadequate or, worse, wrong in their description of reality, they can confine science. Imagine you were to arrive in a strange city and someone were to hand you a wrong map, the map of a different city. You'd have no way to orient yourself to the places marked on the map or find your way to places not marked. You could try however hard – you could drive around, turn the map this way and that, ask directions – but you would have no idea where you were.

History has shown that the same thing can happen in science. Unlike a city map, which surveys a known city, scientific paradigms are often tentative, even speculative, because they map out unknown territory. A paradigm initially successful – and by successful I mean that it gives at least a partly correct description of reality – starts to become untenable when it can no longer account for anomalies. Typically, these anomalies appear only after the paradigm is established and its map has been followed for some time. According to Kuhn, if anomalies accumulate and remain unaccounted for within the paradigmatic structure, the scientific field may experience a "crisis," followed by a "scientific revolution" or "paradigm shift," in which a new paradigm enters to replace the old.

Often, Kuhn pointed out, scientists working within a paradigm no longer adequate are nevertheless still comfortable with it. Either they don't see the anomalies as anomalous, or they don't consider them a problem for the paradigm because they are convinced that with further research the paradigm will be able to account for them. Typically, it's scientists from other fields – or even interested lay scientists – who notice the inadequacy of a paradigm and propose a new one.

A paradigm shift occurred around 1962 in the field of geology when scientists came to accept the idea that each of the earth's continents is part of a large tectonic plate floating on a viscous inner crust. Before 1962 the reigning paradigm, the geosynclinal theory, held that continents were immovable and fixed. After 1962, however, it was understood that the African-Eurasian plate had once been joined to the two American plates but had split off, drifted away, and become three separate continents.

Perhaps this transition between paradigms sounds like it was smooth, but the theory of plate tectonics had first been proposed in the 1920s, and forty years' worth of geologists had considered it untenable. Had they rejected it because it had been propounded by outsiders to the geological community, outsiders like the German meteorologist Alfred Wegener? As late as 1960, geologists Thomas H. Clark and Colin W. Stearn wrote:

> The geosynclinal theory is one of the great unifying principles in geology. In many ways its role in geology is similar to that of the theory of evolution, which serves to integrate the many branches of the biological sciences.... Just as the doctrine of evolution is universally accepted among biologists, so also the geosynclinal origin of the major mountain systems is an established principle in geology.[1]

Only two years after this confident pronouncement, the geosynclinal theory was dropped.

I predict that Darwin's theory is headed for a similar fate. The example of plate tectonics shows that although scientists in the field of evolution are as convinced about Darwinism as ever, this doesn't keep the theory from being in crisis. In fact, we can expect that the mainstream biological community will be among the last to admit that their paradigm is overweighted by anomalies.

As Kuhn observes, even when scientists suspect that an existing paradigm is outmoded they generally cling to it until offered something better. Skeptics of a reigning paradigm must therefore also investigate and propose new ones. Here, therefore, I would like to explore and offer an alternative paradigm based on the philosophy of nature found in ancient India's Vedic literature. Of course, one might question the wisdom of drawing on sacred texts when discussing science. But why reject possibly valid insights simply because of their source? Ideas should be examined on their own merit, no matter where they come from, including religious sources. Valid ideas will stand, and mistaken ones will eventually fall by the weight of their own errors.

The Original Source of Everything, Part One

Modern science starts with systematic empirical observations and then tries to work its way up through different causes and effects to build a picture of reality. Vedic philosophy takes a different approach. It starts by discussing the nature of an original cause behind all existence. In other words, the first step in Vedic philosophy is to sort out what possible explanations may account for where everything has come from. After having assessed the different possibilities for the nature of the original cause, one is then able, according to this Vedic approach, to compare each possibility against the evidence of the world to see which kind of original nature best explains what we observe.

Now, when we speak of an original cause behind existence, by definition that cause must itself have no cause; if it did have a cause, the original wouldn't be original. Furthermore, when we come to the original cause there are basically two possibilities: either everything has come from something that has always existed, or everything has come from nothing.

If at this point we ask which of these two possibilities must logically be the cause behind existence, we might quite well conclude that neither appears logical. Rather, both seem counterintuitive and illogical. How can something come from nothing? But how can something have existed always? Yet counterintuitive or not, one of the two has to be true, because when we come to an original cause behind existence there are only these two logical possibilities: either the uncaused cause is something or it is nothing. There is no third option.

The Vedic philosophy, however, dismisses the possibility that everything comes from nothing. How? By another logical step, called the logic of the relationship between the part and the whole. According to this logic, nothing fundamental can be found in a part that is not found in the whole. For instance, when we analyze a drop of seawater and find it fundamentally salty, we safely assume that as the drop contains salt, so must its origin, the sea. By analyzing the sample, the part, we gain an understanding of what the nature of the whole must minimally be.

This world is likewise a part or sample of the original cause from which it comes. Whatever is fundamental to this world must also be present in that original cause. The Vedic methodology therefore now directs us to have a look at what is fundamental in this world to gain an idea of what the nature of the original cause must be.

Three Categories of Nature

What does the observable evidence tell us about the world? How many fundamental categories does nature consist of? The present materialistic paradigm recognizes only one ultimate category, matter (or matter/energy). But the topics we have examined in this book suggest, I propose, that what we observe in nature points not to one but to three different categories: matter, consciousness, and superconsciousness.

I derive these categories from the Vedic understanding of nature, as expressed, for example, in the *Vishnu Purana*.[2] According to this Vedic understanding, a living organism consists not only of a physical body – a body made of matter – but of a nonphysical conscious being (soul) whose consciousness pervades the body. Further, the physical body and the conscious self are both pervaded by a superconsciousness, a superior conscious self whose intelligence not only guides and inspires the living being but permeates and controls the entire cosmos.

Evidence of intelligent design points to something more than matter – something intelligent – behind nature; self-analysis, near-death-experiences, and memories of previous incarnations point to nonphysical consciousness; and phenomena like inspiration and instinct suggest that besides an individual conscious self there is a separate and superior guiding intelligence at work in the world, moment to moment.

> **Consciousness has the power to direct and organize matter, but matter ultimately works only under conscious direction.**

The Vedic literature calls the superior, guiding, all-pervading intelligence the "Paramatma," or the Supersoul. The Paramatma saturates matter and "sits" beside each embodied conscious self, regardless of what type of body that self inhabits. The self and the Superself, soul and Supersoul, are compared to two birds sitting on the tree of the body, the soul striving to "enjoy the tree's fruits" in the form of mental and sensory input, the Supersoul simply witnessing the soul's activities and controlling the body's activities and functions.

The Original Source of Everything, Part Two

If this world fundamentally consists of matter, consciousness, and superconsciousness, these must also exist in the original cause. But since the original cause can only be one and not two or three, the question still remains whether that original cause is matter or consciousness. Here the Vedic literature, while recognizing physical nature as an immediate cause, points out that physical nature – matter – cannot be the *original* cause.

Why? For two reasons. First, matter is by nature impermanent. Any material thing always has a beginning and an end. And how can the original cause be something that starts out by not even existing? But consciousness, in the Vedic analysis, is by nature permanent. It is both beginningless and endless. No laboratory has ever been able to "create" consciousness, and the Vedic literature says that consciousness is so subtle that no material thing can ever destroy it. It always exists.

The second reason is the same one that forms a main theme of this book: Consciousness has the power to direct and organize matter, but matter ultimately works only under conscious direction. A car works only when a living person drives it. Even a superintelligent car, driven only by a computer, would need a person to write its code and start its programs.

The Vedic literature asserts, therefore, that the original cause of everything is indeed consciousness. At this, one could still ask, Whose consciousness? Mine? Yours? The Vedic literature answers that we cannot plausibly say that each and every consciousness is the original consciousness. We humans each have only limited consciousness, confined within our particular body; we are certainly not all-pervadingly superconscious. We could argue, of course, that somehow we are not aware of our all-pervasive nature but will realize it when we become enlightened. The Vedic literature rejects this argument; to be unaware of being all-pervadingly conscious is simply a contradiction in terms.

All in all, the Vedic literature concludes that the original cause of everything is a conscious being of unfathomable nature existing behind time, space, and matter – in other words, God. The Paramatma, the Supersoul or Superself, is in essence not different from God; it represents the superconscious presence of God within the material world. And for our part, we are simply tiny sparks of eternal consciousness, small parts of the infinite nature of God's all-encompassing consciousness.

Consciousness and personality are practically synonymous, in that consciousness involves self-awareness and this of course implies that there is a self, or person, to be aware and to be aware of. Thus Vedic logic leads to the understanding that the uncaused cause is in essence a person. It also implies that personality is fundamental to existence and not a later emergence from matter.

According to the Vedic concept, God is a person just as the living beings are. The living beings are His minute expansions, though infinitely smaller in power. The soul, as an eternal, inseparable, subordinate part of God, is eternal as is He. Yet God is the controller and maintainer whereas the living beings are the controlled and maintained.

That God has infinite power means He has infinite freedom, whereas the living beings have only a small amount of that freedom. God in His infinite freedom is independent; the living entities with their limited freedom always remain under God's control.

And as for matter, it is an energy of God and controlled by Him. The physical laws are thus not absolute in that they are ultimately controlled by God. They are regulations God has imposed on the physical world, but God, being free, is also free to overstep His regulations wherever and whenever He likes.

Science and Religion

Here we might again ask ourselves what place a discussion about the nature of God has in a book on science. Isn't religion supposed to stay out of science? According to Stephen Jay Gould, religion and science should remain separate because they occupy two completely different realms. He put forward what he described as "a blessedly simple and entirely conventional resolution to … the supposed conflict between science and religion":

> [T]he magisterium of science covers the empirical realm: what the universe is made of (fact) and why does it work in this way (theory). The magisterium of religion extends over questions of ultimate meaning and moral value. These two magisteria do not overlap.[3]

Since Gould felt that religion and science do not overlap, he considered it improper to introduce religious ideas, such as the notion of God's existence, into discussions on science.

But religion is not obliged to confine itself to issues of meaning and moral value; most religious thought also has specific ideas about the nature of the world. Neither does what science says about life and the world lack implications for our understanding of ultimate meaning or moral values.

If, for instance, we are told that life and personality are illusory secondary effects of interactions of material elements, what ultimate meaning is left for religion to assign to life? After all, meaning can only be ascribed in relation to persons or what a thing can do for a person; matter in and of itself has no inherent meaning. If there is nothing ultimate, what ultimate meaning can religion ascribe to anything?

Or if we are told, again in the name of science, that life, as we see it now, arose out of a ruthless struggle for survival where the stronger got rid of the weaker, what moral value would that leave for, say, altruism? Altruism would simply be an anachronism standing in the way of further evolutionary advancement.

Clearly, that science and religion occupy two different "magisteriums," as Gould would have it, is not self-evident. I see no just reason to grant Gould and his monopolistic colleagues one hundred percent of reality, leaving the rest of us to share between us whatever is left.

And Gould's objection is a relatively modern one. Science and religion have not always been seen as two different areas of study by either scientists or leaders in religion. Scientific discoveries were once viewed as supportive of religious ideas, and scientists also drew on and were inspired by religious concepts in their search for truth. In Newton's *Principia*, for example, a work that has served as the cornerstone of modern science, we find this:

> [T]his most beautiful system of the sun, planets, and comets could only proceed from the counsel and dominion of an intelligent and powerful Being.[4]

Newton argued that although the movements of the planets could be explained by physical laws – the laws of motion and gravity, principally – the orderliness of their movements pointed to an intelligent being behind them. Newton did not consider this conclusion outside the realm of science.

As late as 1857, only two years before Darwin published *Origin*, Louis Agassiz, professor at Harvard and one of the leading biologists in the world at that time, wrote that the living world

> shows also premeditation, wisdom, greatness, prescience, omniscience, providence ... all these facts ... proclaim aloud the One God whom man may know, and natural history must, in good time, become the analysis of the thoughts of the Creator of the Universe, as manifested in the animal and vegetable kingdoms, as well as in the inorganic world.[5]

Science to become the "analysis of the thoughts of the Creator"? But Agassiz's ideal of understanding God through science was in his time not at all considered controversial or heretical. Of course, two years later, when Darwin published his evolutionary theory and ushered into the world of science the modern era of materialism, all this was destined to change.

Yet even though Darwin's materialistic adherents speak of wanting to keep discussion of God and religion out of the scientific domain, in reality their ideas teem with concealed religious arguments. Often these take the form of "God would never have created this feature [behavior, trait, disease] like that. Therefore this feature must have been the 'creation' of random and mindless evolution." Darwin himself said,

> [If species have evolved] we need not marvel at the sting of the bee causing the bee's own death; at drones being produced in such vast numbers for one single act, and being then slaughtered by their sterile sisters; at the astonishing waste of pollen by our fir trees; at the instinctive hatred of the queen bee for her

own fertile daughters; at ichneumonidae [wasps] feeding within the live bodies of caterpillars; and at other such cases.[6]

Darwin's *Origin of Species* is one long argument about why it is more plausible that species have evolved naturally by descent from one or a few original life forms than that they were separately created. Here he states one of his arguments baldly: A creator would not have created bees with barbed stingers that stay hooked in the creature stung and rip open the bee's own body and kill it as the bee pulls away. What kind of God would create something like that? Darwin concludes that nature, therefore, in its own blind way, must have evolved like that. Clearly, his theory has theological underpinnings.

In more recent times, in a discussion on the origin of the panda's thumb (see pp. 56, 77) and other peculiar features in nature, Stephen J. Gould wrote:

Odd arrangements and funny solutions are the proof of evolution – paths that a sensible God would never tread.[7]

And so the same Gould who speaks of keeping science and religion strictly apart seems comfortable mixing them to argue against God's involvement with nature.

In 2005 Douglas J. Futuyma wrote in the college textbook *Evolution,* "There are many examples, such as the eyes of vertebrates and cephalopod molluscs, in which functionally similar features actually differ profoundly in structure. Such differences are expected if structures are modified from features that differ in different ancestors, but are inconsistent with the notion that an omnipotent Creator, who should be able to adhere to an optimal design, provided them."[8]

"Should be able to"? Let's leave aside the question of how much an omnipotent Creator should be expected to adhere to what Gould and Futuyma regard as an optimal design. The real point here is, Why do these scientists, supposedly so intent on keeping science and religion separate, keep introducing discussions of God into their science?

The reason, I suggest, is that this whole idea of wanting to keep science and religion separate is artificial. From the material discussed in this book, it is evident that concepts of God, the soul, and creation continue to pop up in scientific discussions despite attempts to pretend otherwise. Perhaps the reason for this is that science and religion are not really separate fields, as Gould would have it, but complementary and integral parts of the same scientific discussion about the nature of reality.

Theodicy – the Problem of Evil

One theological issue both Darwin and his followers seem to view as a strong argument in favor of natural evolution is the dichotomy between a benevolent and almighty God and the seemingly meaningless suffering in the world. Darwin wrote,

> I cannot see as plainly as others do, and as I should wish to do, evidence of design and beneficence on all sides of us. There seems to me too much misery in the world. I cannot persuade myself that a beneficent and omnipotent God would have designedly created the Ichneumonidae with the express intention of their [larva] feeding within the living bodies of Caterpillars, or that a cat should play with mice.[9]

In 2005 Harvard evolutionary psychology professor Steve Pinker expressed the same problem:

> Our bodies are riddled with quirks that no competent engineer would have planned but that disclose a history of trial and error tinkering; a retina installed backward, a seminal duct that hooks over the ureter like a garden hose snagged on a tree, goose bumps that uselessly try to warm us by fluffing up long-gone fur. The moral design of nature is as bungled as its engineering design. What twisted sadist would have intended a parasite

that blinds millions of people or a gene that covers babies with excruciating blisters?[10]

Similarly, Richard Dawkins:

> The universe we observe has precisely the properties we should expect if there is, at bottom, no design, no purpose, no evil, and no good – nothing but blind, pitiless indifference.[11]

Since the issue of evil and imperfection seems to keep being raised in arguments in favor of evolution, let us see what the Vedic philosophy has to say about it. According to the Vedic literature, the world's suffering is due neither to an absence of God nor to divine incompetence or viciousness. God is infinitely kind and loving, but something else is at work. To see this we need to look at the Vedic concept of two worlds.

The *Bhagavad-gita* says that beyond the material existence in which we live, where all is continually created and destroyed, lies another reality, another world.

> It is supreme and is never annihilated. When all in this world is annihilated, that part remains as it is.[12]

This implies that the conscious selves of the organisms who inhabit this world are actually foreign to it. Instead, these souls belong to the nonmaterial, spiritual world, and the cause of their suffering here is that they don't belong here.

According to the Vedic concept, the spiritual world is a spiritual dimension, constituting the major portion of the total reality. And it is there that the vast majority of souls exist. Only a relative few have become entangled in the material world in the bodies of plants, animals, or humans. And their entanglement in the material world is due not to God but to their misuse of their own free will.

According to the *Vedas*, the souls in the spiritual world live with God in an intimate and free relationship of love. Love implies freedom; love must be freely given, and can be neither demanded nor purchased. As soon as there is some form of coercion, love dies.

Souls, therefore, can choose *not* to have an intimate loving relationship with God but instead to make their own enjoyment their purpose of existence. This desire for self-pleasure reflects a kind of envy of God, the supreme enjoyer. As explained in *Vedanta Psychology,* "Our basic desire, the one that brought us to the material world, is to enjoy or control, or in other words, *to be* God."[13]

For the tiny soul to divorce himself from God and independently control and enjoy is simply not existentially possible. It could be possible only in an illusion. And so, to accommodate souls who want it, God creates a world of illusion – the world in which we now live. This means not that the world doesn't exist but that it appears

> **Vedic evolution is not about one body changing into another body, but about an evolution of consciousness.**

to be something other than it is. It appears to be a place detached from God where we can enjoy and find permanent meaning, but in fact it is a place where we forget our eternal nature and where, pursuing enjoyment, we inevitably suffer. Trying to master and exploit the resources of the world, we become trapped in it. And while trying to exploit, we cause suffering for others, suffering that eventually comes back on us.

The problem with the world, therefore, is not that it is poorly designed but that it's the wrong place for us, a place where we don't belong, a world to which the soul has insisted on coming but which the Vedic literature advises can never be our real home.

The *Bhagavad-gita,* in fact, advises that we should be ever aware of the miseries of this world, not to complain of them as evidence for the nonexistence of God but to recognize that the purpose of human life is to get free from them by reviving our relationship with God.

Vedic Evolution – the Evolution of Consciousness

Darwin's thesis that the patterns he observed in nature point to natural evolutionary processes and not to special creation, in which God creates all species separately, obviously involves theological considerations, if only because it suggests what God did *not* do.

The Vedic outlook involves both special creation and also a kind of evolution. The Vedic idea of evolution differs from the materialistic evolution of Darwin's theory, but it also accounts for certain evolutionary patterns seen in nature. Contrary to what Darwin thought, evolutionary patterns need not proceed only from natural causes.

Vedic evolution is not about one body changing into another body as in Darwinian evolution, but about an evolution of consciousness, in which the species themselves are static but the souls within them move, at the end of each lifetime, from one body to the next, and from one species to the next.

According to the Vedic account, all souls originate in the greater spiritual universe, where they exist with their full natural consciousness and intelligence, but when they misuse their freedom and fall into the physical universe their consciousness is covered to greater or lesser degrees. Once here, they migrate through the species according to their consciousness and desires.

In the part of the physical world that is visible to us, the Vedic teachings say, evolution moves mainly in an upward direction. Souls embodied in plant and animal species are so restricted by the body that they can hardly make willful choices. They are very much under nature's laws as we know them and have no ability to violate them. And so, by natural subtle laws, these souls move up through the various species until they reach the human form.

But when these souls achieve a human body, the Vedic literature says, their natural consciousness has the opportunity to blossom, and they again have the freedom to choose more than just what to eat or how to defend themselves. They can choose, for example, to search for the truth about themselves and their world. But they can also choose to misuse their greater consciousness and intelligence by dedicating it to more effectively exploiting matter's resources.

With greater freedom comes greater responsibility, and souls in human bodies are therefore at a juncture where either they may continue to evolve upwards or they may devolve toward the lower species. Some souls are fortunate enough to grasp the point of their human freedom, others not. Those who grasp it fully and reestablish their awareness of their spiritual nature in relation to God return to the spiritual world. Those who grasp it only partially may continue to evolve upwards to subtler dimensions in the material universe or be born again in a human form after the death of their current body. Those who don't grasp the point of the human form at all generally return to the lower species to live out their gross physical desires.

So parallel to evolution is devolution. That is, some souls evolve upwards through the species toward the human form, yet others, from there, may degrade themselves.

It would seem that Alfred Russel Wallace's idea (see pp. 178–79) that the evolution of species is a divinely guided process meant to accommodate spiritual beings in physical bodies as they engage in an ongoing spiritual evolution is not far from the Vedic conception.

Furthermore, the Vedic literature tells us that the physical species, although created separately, are paradoxically related not only through common design but also through a kind of common ancestry. In Darwin's theory the common ancestor of all beings is the most simple of organisms, but in the Vedic account the common ancestor is the most advanced of all beings.

Here the Vedic literature refers not to God but to a secondary material creator, Brahma, who after the primary creation is entrusted with the task of populating the universe. Brahma, who exists in a subtler dimension, does his work by creating from his body a variety of beings, who in turn create other beings. Some of these are the first to procreate sexually. Some have the power to procreate not only their own kind but other species as well, each of which then goes on to reproduce only its own kind. This creates a unique blend of design and sexual procreation.

Thus humans and apes, for instance, may indeed be related through common ancestry, although the common ancestor is not a more primitive primate but a being of a higher nature existing in a realm not visible to us. Still, common ancestry is common ancestry, and it may explain why certain physical evidence actually points to common descent.

Here I have only sketched in briefest outline some Vedic ideas about creation and evolution. I suggest, however, that the Vedic paradigm can not only account for the anomalies in Darwin's theory but incorporate whatever truth there may be in evolutionism, albeit in a way evolutionary biologists have probably not considered.

Concluding Words

I remember when I too was convinced about natural evolution. When I first encountered a critique of Darwin I was startled. I was reading a book of Srila Prabhupada's published in the mid 1970s called *Life Comes From Life*, which consists of animated discussions between Prabhupada and the chemist Dr. Thoudam Singh. Although Prabhupada himself was not without a background in chemistry, he chose to argue like a layman. "We always see that life comes from life," he said. "We have never seen life come from dead matter. Doesn't that suggest that the origin of life is life and not matter?" And, "They claim life came from chemicals, but when asked for a demonstration they have no idea except to say they'll do it in the future. What kind of science is this?"

My curiosity was aroused both by the obviousness of Prabhupada's arguments and by their power to stymie a Ph.D. in chemistry. The arguments sowed a seed of doubt in me, and as I proceeded to study the subject in more depth I had to admit that evolution did not seem to stand up to close scrutiny.

In 1976 Prabhupada founded the Bhaktivedanta Institute (BI), with Thoudam Singh as one of its first active researchers, to explore the borders between traditional Vedic philosophy and modern science. As a result, starting in the late 1970s and continuing through the '80s and '90s, BI members published a number of books and papers, prominent among them *Consciousness: The Missing Link*, *Mechanistic and Non-Mechanistic Science*, *Darwin's Secret Identity*, and *Origins*. However, except for Michael Cremo and Richard Thompson's *Forbidden Archeology*, which has sold briskly and occasioned much discussion since 1993, most of the BI's work has been unnoticed except by those already delving into Vedic philosophy.

To be a Darwin skeptic in the 1970s was rare, even a little lonely. But in the late 1980s I began to notice the Intelligent Design movement – a movement rooted in the early '80s that has risen to prominence through the '90s. There I saw that another group of scientists and intellectuals had independently developed the same kinds of arguments with which I had become familiar through the BI's publications.

Of course, I was already aware of the Christian creationists who speak against Darwin. Although not a Christian myself, I could appreciate parts of their critique of evolution (aside from their arguments for a young earth). When the ID movement gained attention, its critics tried to brush it off as closet creationism. But I could see that it was clearly something else. First, the ideas ID scientists proposed came from a different brand of intellectuals; second, and more importantly, ID offered a different concept and approach. While creationists argue from the Bible, attempting to demonstrate the Bible's validity by finding corroborating material evidence, the ID people argue from empirical observation and note that material processes are insufficient to explain certain features of life. Theirs were the same scientific arguments for design I had already become familiar with from the BI.

Of course, the BI has often gone further than core ID scientists in that BI scientists have included discussions on consciousness, reincarnation, and the like. Still, the similarity between the two groups is striking. Even the term "intelligent design" was in use at the BI before it came into vogue through the ID movement. For instance, as early as 1976, in a presentation to Prabhupada and others involved with the BI, Richard Thompson discussed the then recently discovered bacterial flagellum. At one point Dr. Thompson said:

> We'd like to argue that the chance and molecular forces theory won't explain things like this but to say that there is an *intelligent designer* would be a sensible explanation.[14]

The terms "intelligent design" and "intelligent designer" later appeared regularly in publications by BI researchers long before they rose to public awareness through the ID movement. Of course, this does not mean that the BI invented these terms – the terms go back at least as far as the eighteenth century. And from what I have been able to gather, there were no inspirational connections between the BI and those who later started the ID movement. The two seem to have evolved independently of one another, although both in response to the failings of evolutionary theory.

In any case, I began to interact with the ID people and found the association both fruitful and stimulating. This book is one result of that association.

This book is the first of its kind in that although I use the same overall approach normally used by the BI, I have tried to blend material from both groups. Indeed, one goal of my book has been to present to audiences normally reached only by the BI how the ID people demonstrate the inadequacy of Darwin's theory and the concept of natural evolution. If the book can also inform the ID movement of some of the ideas from the BI, then so much the better.

In the introduction to this book I mentioned a quotation from Theodore Dobzhansky: "Nothing in biology makes sense except in the light of evolution." It was one of my goals in the writing to show that a Vedic model could enable us to formulate an alternative theory to evolution, one that offers another light to see by, one that is perhaps even better. It is my humble hope that I have given at least a hint of another way of thinking about biology.

Prabhupada said very simply, "Modern scientists are of the opinion that life comes from matter. We say, 'No, life comes from life, and matter comes from life.'"[15] This is the essence of the Vedic understanding of nature, an understanding Prabhupada proposed could replace the failed ideas of Darwin.

Notes

Introduction

1. Mayr's speech is freely available on the Internet (as of June 2008) at www.
   biologie.uni-hamburg.de/b-online/e36_2/darwin_influence.htm.
2. Ayala, "Darwin's Greatest Discovery: Design Without Designer," 8567–8573.
3. Dawkins, *The Blind Watchmaker*, 6.
4. Darwin, C., *On the Origin of Species by Means of Natural Selection or the Preservation of Favoured Races in the Struggle for Life* was first published by John Murray in 1859. I have used Penguin Books' 1985 edition as my reference. Here, 459–60.
5. Dobzhansky, "*Nothing in Biology Makes Sense Except in the Light of Evolution*," 125–129.
6. Oftentimes the word *Vedic* is used to strictly denote the four original *Vedas*, namely, the *Rig*, *Yajur*, *Sama*, and *Atharva Vedas*. But here I have used the term in a broader sense to include the *Puranas*, *Itihasas*, *Mahabharata*, *Bhagavad-gita*, etc.
7. Sagan, *Cosmos*, 258.
8. Dr. Urey is famous for the Miller-Urey experiment. See p. 31 in this book.

Chapter 1   The Origin of Species

1. Darwin, F., *The Life and Letters of Charles Darwin*, vol. 1, 45.
2. Darwin, C., *The Voyage of the Beagle*, 382.
3. Darwin, F., *The Life and Letters of Charles Darwin*, vol. 2, 23.
4. For a good summary of this event, see Ross A. Slotten's *The Heretic in Darwin's*

Court: The Life of Alfred Russel Wallace, New York: Columbia University Press, 2004, 153–61.

5. Darwin, C., *On the Origin of Species*, 57: "The celebrated geologist and naturalist, Von Buch, in his excellent 'Description Physique des Isles Canaries' (1836, 147), clearly expresses his belief that varieties slowly become changed into permanent species, which are no longer capable of intercrossing."

6. Darwin, C., *On the Origin of Species*, 155.

7. Macbeth, *Darwin Retried*, 36.

8. Johnson, *Darwin on Trial*, 18.

9. Hitching, *The Neck of the Giraffe*, 54.

10. Darwin, C., *On the Origin of Species*, 76.

11. De Vries, *The Mutation Theory*, Vol. II, 185.

12. Darwin, C., *Origin of Species*, 132.

13. ibid., 74.

14. ibid., 175.

15. ibid., 72.

16. Mendel, "Versuche über Pflanzen-Hybriden," 3–47.

17. Wells, *The Politically Incorrect Guide to Darwinism and Intelligent Design*, 72–73.

18. Wills, *The Runaway Brain*, xxii.

19. As a footnote to the rejected idea of pangenesis and acquired characteristics, I need to mention that surprisingly, research in recent years has shown that there indeed appears to be at least some kind of inheritance of acquired traits, although the exact nature of that inheritance continues to elude biologists. In the article "A Comeback for Lamarckian Evolution?" published in the *Technology Review* (February 4, 2009) of the Massachusetts Institute of Technology, Emily Singer writes, "Recent studies have shown that the effects of an animal's environment during adolescence can be passed down to future offspring, according to two new studies. If applicable to humans, the research, done on rodents, suggests that the impact of both childhood education and early abuse could span generations. The findings provide support for a 200-year-old theory of evolution that has been largely dismissed: Lamarckian evolution, which states that acquired characteristics can be passed on to offspring. 'The results are extremely surprising and unexpected,' says Li-Huei Tsai, a neuroscientist at MIT who was not involved in the research. Indeed, one of the studies found that a boost in the brain's ability to rewire itself and a corresponding improvement in memory could be passed on. 'This study is probably the first study to show there are transgenerational effects not only on behavior but on brain plasticity.'"

20. West, *Darwin Day in America*, ix.

21. Wallace wrote, "The universal teaching of modern spiritualism is that the world

and the whole material universe exist for the purpose of developing spiritual beings – that death is simply a transition from material existence to the first grade of spirit-life – and that our happiness and the degree of our progress will be wholly dependent upon the use we have made of our faculties and opportunities here." (Quoted from Cremo, *Human Devolution*, 126.)

22. Dawson, *The Christian Commonwealth*, 177.
23. Johnson, *Darwin on Trial*, 152.
24. ibid., 38–39.
25. ibid., 66–67.
26. ibid., 67.
27. Berra, *Evolution and the Myth of Creationism*. Here quoted from Wells, *Icons of Evolution*, 68.
28. The invitation to the conference can be found at www.kli.ac.at/stuff/reports/KLIreport2008.pdf.
29. See, for example, www.talkorigins.org/faqs/faq-speciation.html.
30. One exception to this is polyploidy, or chromosomal mutation, during which, for example, the number of chromosomes in an offspring is doubled from the number of chromosomes in each parent. Polyploidy is especially recognized in plants, and constitutes instances of real speciation leading to new species incapable of interbreeding. However, polyploidy doesn't generate new genetic information but is simply one more way of recombining already existing traits. Thus instances of polyploidy are irrelevant on lists of speciation that happen due to small random changes (point mutations) – the kind of mutations claimed by Neo-Darwinian theory to be the engine of evolution.
31. See Wells, *Icons of Evolution*, 159 ff.
32. Discussed in Patterson, *Evolution*, 105.
33. Dembski and Wells, *The Design of Life*, 102.
34. ibid.

Chapter 2   Survival of the Fakest

This chapter originally appeared as an article in *The American Spectator,* December 2000/January 2001. Printed with permission from Jonathan Wells and the Discovery Institute.

Chapter 3   The Fossil Record

1. National Academy of Sciences, *Science, Evolution and Creationism*, 22.
2. Darwin, C., *On the Origin of Species*, 292.
3. Heribert-Nilsson, *Synthetische Artbildung*, 1212.

4. Raup, "Conflicts Between Darwin and Paleontology," 25.

5. Eldredge, *Reinventing Darwin*, 95.

6. Eldredge, "Paleontology and Evolution," Review of *Evolution: What the Fossils Say and Why It Matters*, Donald R. Prothero, in *Evolution*, vol. 62-6, 1544–1546.

7. Gould, *The Panda's Thumb*, 182.

8. Darwin, C., *On the Origin of Species*, 292.

9. Dembski and Wells, *Design of Life*, 70ff.

10. ibid.

11. Darwin, C., *On the Origin of Species*, 206.

12. See www.fossilmuseum.net/Tree_of_Life/Stromatolites.htm.

13. Futuyma, *Evolutionary Biology*, 146. Here quoted from Dembski and Wells, *Design of Life*, 81.

14. The argument that follows is adapted from Dembski and Wells, *Design of Life*, 83–84.

15. Futuyma, *Science on Trial*, 85. Here quoted from Dembski and Wells, *Design of Life*, 83.

16. *Prum*, "Are Current Critiques of the Therapod Origin of Birds Science?", 559.

17. Shipman, "Birds Do It ... Did Dinosaurs?", 28.

18. Feduccia, Lingham-Soliar, and Hinchcliffe, "Do Feathered Dinosaurs Exist?", 125–166.

19. Martin and Czerkas, "The Fossil Record of Feather Evolution in the Mesozoic," 687.

20. Lingham-Soliar, "A Unique Cross-section Through the Skin of the Dinosaur Psittacosaurus from China Showing a Complex Fibre Architecture," 775–780.

21. Highfield, "Bald Truth About Dinosaur Feathers."

22. Quoted from www.creationsafaris.com/crev200604.htm#fossil201.

23. Wong.

24. Wilford, "Fossil Called Missing Link From Sea to Land Animal."

25. Daeschler et al., "A Devonian Tetrapod-like Fish and the Evolution of the Tetrapod Body Plan," 757–763.

26. Boisvert, Mark-Kurik, and Ahlberg, "The Pectoral Fin of Panderichthys and the Origin of Digits," 636–638.

27. Than, "Ancient Fish Had Primitive Fingers, Toes."

28. Gee, quoted in Wells' *The Politically Incorrect Guide to Darwinism and Intelligent Design*, 20.

29. Stainforth, "Occurrence of Pollen and Spores in the Roraima Formation of Venezuela and British Guiana," 292–294.

30. Leclercq, "Evidence of Vascular Plants in the Cambrian," 109–114.

31. Adapted from Cremo, "Paleobotanical Anomalies Bearing on the Age of the Salt Range Formation of Pakistan: A Historical Survey of an Unresolved Scientific Controversy."

32. Chanda, "Amiya Kumar Ghosh" (obituary), 266–267.

Chapter 4   What is Intelligent Design

1. Davies, *The Fifth Miracle*, 112.

Chapter 5   Convergence

1. Darwin, C., *On the Origin of Species*, 217.
2. Morris, *Life's Solution*, 154.
3. Smith, *Taking a Chance on Evolution*, 34–36.
4. Morris, *Life's Solution*, xv.
5. ibid., 301.
6. ReMine, "Evidence for Message Theory."

Chapter 6   Irreducible Complexity: Obstacle to Darwinian Evolution

1. Behe, 1996.
2. Behe, Reply to my critics: A response to reviews of *Darwin's Black Box: The Biochemical Challenge to Evolution, Biology and Philosophy* 16, 685–709.
3. Darwin, C., *On the Origin of Species*, 158.
4. DeRosier, "The Turn of the Screw: The Bacterial Flagellar Motor," 1998; Shapiro, "The Bacterial Flagellum: From Genetic Network to Complex Architecture," 1995.
5. Yonekura et al., 2000.
6. Harold, *The Way of the Cell*, 205.
7. For example, microbiologist James Shapiro of the University of Chicago declared in the *National Review* that "There are no detailed Darwinian accounts for the evolution of any fundamental biochemical or cellular system, only a variety of wishful speculations." (Shapiro 1996) In *Nature* University of Chicago evolutionary biologist Jerry Coyne stated, "There is no doubt that the pathways described by Behe are dauntingly complex, and their evolution will be hard to unravel.... [W]e may forever be unable to envisage the first proto-pathways." (Coyne 1996) In a particularly scathing review in *Trends in Ecology and Evolution* Tom Cavalier-Smith, an evolutionary biologist at the University of British Columbia, nonetheless wrote, "For none of the cases mentioned by Behe is there yet a comprehensive and detailed explanation of the probable steps in the evolution of the observed complexity. The problems have indeed been sorely neglected – though Behe repeatedly exaggerates this neglect with such hyperboles as 'an eerie and complete silence.'" (Cavalier-Smith 1997) Evolutionary biologist Andrew Pomiankowski agreed in *New Scientist*, "Pick up

any biochemistry textbook, and you will find perhaps two or three references to evolution. Turn to one of these and you will be lucky to find anything better than 'evolution selects the fittest molecules for their biological function.'" (Pomiankowski 1996) In *American Scientist* Yale molecular biologist Robert Dorit averred, "In a narrow sense, Behe is correct when he argues that we do not yet fully understand the evolution of the flagellar motor or the blood clotting cascade." (Dorit 1997)

8. A good example is found on the "World of Richard Dawkins" website maintained by Dawkins fan John Catalano at www.world-of-dawkins.com/ Catalano/box/published.htm. It is to this site that Oxford University physical chemist Peter Atkins was referring when he wrote in a review of *Darwin's Black Box* for the Infidels website, "Dr. Behe claims that science is largely silent on the details of molecular evolution, the emergence of complex biochemical pathways and processes that underlie the more traditional manifestations of evolution at the level of organisms. Tosh! There are hundreds, possibly thousands, of scientific papers that deal with this very subject. For an entry into this important and flourishing field, and an idea of the intense scientific effort that it represents (see the first link above) [*sic*]." (Atkins 1998)

9. Dawkins, *The Blind Watchmaker*, 6.

10. Miller, *Finding Darwin's God*, 253.

11. Kauffman, *At Home in the Universe*, viii.

12. Miller, *Finding Darwin's God*, 241.

13. Behe, *Darwin's Black Box*, 53.

14. Dutcher, "Flagellar Assembly in Two Hundred and Fifty Easy-to-follow Steps," *Trends in Genetics* 11, 398–404.

15. Behe, *Darwin's Black Box*, 60.

16. Miller, *Finding Darwin's God*, 140–43.

17. Aizawa, "Assembly in Salmonella Typhimurium," *Molecular Microbiology* 19, 1–5.

18. See Hueck, "Type III Protein Secretion Systems in Bacterial Pathogens of Animals and Plants."

19. Behe, *Darwin's Black Box*, 74–97.

20. Halkier, "Mechanisms in Blood Coagulation Fibrinolysis and the Complement System."

21. Bugge et al. (1996a).

22. Doolittle, "A Delicate Balance," *Boston Review*, Feb/March 1997, 28–29.

23. Bugge et al. (1996a) were interested in the question of whether plasminogen had any role in metabolism other than its role in clotting, as had been postulated. The fact that the direct effects of plasminogen deficiency were ameliorated by fibrinogen deficiency showed that plasminogen likely had no other role.

24. Ruse, "Answering the Creationists: Where They Go Wrong and What They're Afraid Of," *Free Inquiry,* March 22, 1998, 28.

25. Greenspan, "Not-So-Intelligent Design," *The Scientist* 16, 12.

26. udel.edu/~mcdonald/oldmousetrap.html. Professor McDonald has recently designed a new series of traps, which can be seen at udel.edu/~mcdonald/mousetrap.html. I have examined them and have concluded that they involve his directing intelligence to the same degree.

27. Behe, *Darwin's Black Box,* 43.

28. Behe, "A Mousetrap Defended: Response to Critics," www.crsc.org.

29. A proteome is the complement of proteins in an organism.

30. Gavin et al., "Functional Organization of the Yeast Proteome by Systematic Analysis of Protein Complexes," *Nature* 415, 141–147.

31. Alberts, *Cell* 92, 291–294.

Chapter 7   The Origin of Life

1. Although normally dated 1871, some refer to a letter from Charles Darwin to Joseph Hooker dated March 29, 1863.

2. Rehbock, "Huxley, Haeckel, and the Oceanographers," 504–533.

3. "Semi-Creation," *Time,* May 25, 1953.

4. Morris, *Life's Solution,* 44.

5. What follows is largely adapted from Dembski and Wells, *The Design of Life,* 207 ff.

6. See Wells, *Icons of Evolution,* 14–17.

7. Ibid., 17.

8. Ibid., 20.

9. Thaxton, Bradley, and Olsen, *The Mystery of Life's Origin,* 57.

10. Brooks and Shaw, *Origin and Development of Living Systems,* 359.

11. Horgan, "In the Beginning ... ," 100–109.

12. Joyce, "The Antiquity of RNA-based Evolution," 215.

13. Joyce and Orgel, *The RNA World,* 68.

14. Shapiro, "A Simpler Origin for Life," *Scientific American,* June 2007, 24–31.

15. Orgel, "The Implausibility of Metabolic Cycles on the Prebiotic Earth," e18.

16. Ibid.

17. Whitesides, "Revolutions in Chemistry."

18. Gates, *The Road Ahead,* 228.

19. Polanyi, "Life Transcending Physics and Chemistry," *Chemical & Engineering News,* August 21, 1967, 62.

Chapter 8   The Molecular Evidence

1. *Science, Evolution, and Creationism,* National Academy of Sciences, 28.
2. The example of equidistance has been adapted from Denton's *Evolution: A Theory in Crisis,* 274–307.
3. The following discussions have been adapted from Dembski and Wells, *The Design of Life,* 126–131.
4. Aguinaldo, "Evidence for A Clade of Nematodes, Arthropods, and Other Moulting Animals: New Perspectives on the Cambrian Explosion," 489–493.
5. Lynch, "The Age and Relationships of the Major Animal Phyla," 319–25.
6. Adoutte et al., "The New Animal Phylogeny: Reliability and Implications," 4453–4456.
7. Blair et al., "The Evolutionary Position of Nematodes," 7.
8. Wolf et al., "Coelomata and Not Ecdysozoa: Evidence From Genome-Wide Phylogenetic Analysis," 29–36.
9. Philippe et al., "Multigene Analysis of Bilaterian Animals Corroborate the Monophyly of Ecdysozoa, Lophotrochozoa, and Protostomia," 1246–1253.
10. Jones and Blaxter, "Animal Roots and Shoots," 1076–1077.
11. Rokas et al., "Animal Evolution and the Molecular Signature of Radiations Compressed in Time," 1933–1938.
12. Lake et al., "Mix and Match in the Tree of Life," 2027–2028.
13. Philippe and Forterre, "The Rooting of the Universal Tree of Life Is Not Reliable," 509–523.
14. Woese, "The Universal Ancestor," 6854–6859.
15. Doolittle, "Uprooting the Tree of Life," 90–95.
16. Philippe and Forterre, "Where Is the Root of the Universal Tree of Life," 871–879.
17. Woese, "A New Biology for a New Century," 173–186.
18. See note 1.
19. Adapted from Cremo, *Human Devolution,* 82–95.
20. This may be a truth with some modification. Studies show that the tail of the sperm cell, which is enclosed in the egg cell, also contains some mitochondrial DNA. Thus the father may also contribute to the mitochondrial DNA in the progeny. This was discussed in a paper from 1996 in Proceedings of the National Academy of Sciences (Ankel-Simons and Cummins, "Misconceptions about mitochondria and mammalian fertilization: Implications for theories on human evolution," 13859–13863). However, newer studies now show that although this is correct it also appears that all paternal mitochondrial DNA is nevertheless destroyed by various processes during fertilization before becoming a part of the cells of the progeny (see Nishimura et al., "Active

Digestion of Sperm Mitochondrial DNA in Single Living Sperm Revealed by Optical Tweezers," 1382–1387). According to Nishimura et al., it can thus still be concluded that all mitochondrial DNA stems from the mother.

21. Cann, Stoneking, and Wilson, *Mitochondrial DNA and Human Evolution*, 31–36.
22. Vigilant, Stoneking, Harpending, Hawkes, and Wilson, "African Populations and the Evolution of Human Mitochondrial DNA," 1503–1507.
23. Templeton, "The 'Eve' Hypothesis: A Genetic Critique and Reanalysis," 52.
24. Templeton, "Human Origins and Analysis of Mitochondrial DNA Sequences," 737.
25. Templeton, "The 'Eve' Hypothesis: A Genetic Critique and Reanalysis," 52.
26. Cremo, *Human Devolution*, 85–86.
27. Ibid., 86–87.
28. Gibbons, "Modern Men Trace Ancestry to African Migrants," 1052.

Chapter 9   Human Origins and the Archeological Record

1. Leakey, M., "Footprints in the Ashes of Time," *National Geographic* 155, 446–457.
2. Tuttle, "Ape Footprints and Laetoli Impressions: a Response to the SUNY Claims."
3. Steen-McIntyre et al., "Geologic Evidence for Age of Deposits at Hueyatlaco Archaeological Site, Valsequillo, Mexico," *Quaternary Research* 16: 1–17.
4. Cremo and Thompson, *Forbidden Archeology*, 364–65.
5. Whitney, "The Auriferous Gravels of the Sierra Nevada of California, *Harvard University, Museum of Comparative Zoology Memoir* 6(1).
6. Slemmons, "Cenozoic Volcanism of the Central Sierra Nevada, California," *Bulletin of the California Division of Mines and Geology* 190, 199–208.
7. Holmes, "Review of the Evidence Relating to Auriferous Gravel Man in California," *Smithsonian Institution Annual Report 1898–1899*, 419–4721899, 424).
8. Cremo, *Forbidden Archeology's Impact*, 467–534.
9. Winchell, *Sparks from a Geologist's Hammer*, 170.
10. Personal communication, 1984; Cremo and Thompson, *Forbidden Archeology*, 801–802.
11. Wright, *Origin and Antiquity of Man*, 266–267.
12. Silliman, "Curious Geological Facts", *American Journal of Science and Arts* 2, 145-146.
13. Pomerol, *Geology of France*, 172–173.
14. Day and Molleson, "The Trinil Femora," *Symposia of the Society for the Study of Human Biology* 2, 151.

15. Jacob, "Palaeoanthropological Discoveries in Indonesia With Special Reference to Finds of the Last Two Decades," *Journal of Human Evolution* 2, 477.

16. Leakey, R., "Skull 1470," *National Geographic* 143, 821.

17. Johanson et al., "New Partial Skeleton of *Homo habilis* from Olduvai Gorge, Tanzania," *Nature* 327, 205–209.

18. Patterson and Howells, "Hominid Humeral Fragment from Early Pleistocene of Northwestern Kenya," *Science* 156, 64–66.

19. Chavaillon et al., "Présence d'hominidé dans le site oldowayen de Gomboré I à Melka Kunturé, Éthiopie," *Comptes Rendus de l'Académie des Sciences,* Series D 285, 961–963.

20. Wood, "Evidence on the Locomotor Pattern of *Homo* From Early Pleistocene of Kenya," *Nature* 251, 135–136.

21. Hrdlička, *Early man in South America,* 318.

22. Ibid., 332.

23. Ibid., 321.

24. Anderson, "Who's Who in the Pleistocene: A Mammalian Bestiary, 41; Marshall et al., "Mammalian Evolution and the Great American Interchange," *Science* 215, 1352.

25. Reck, "Erste vorläufige Mitteilungen über den Fund eines fossilen Menschenskeletts aus Zentral-afrika."

26. Protsch, "The Age and Stratigraphic Position of Olduvai Hominid I," *Journal of Human Evolution* 3, 397–385.

27. Harding, "History of Modern Man Unravels as German Scholar is Exposed as Fraud," *The Guardian,* February 19, 2005.

28. Osborn, "The Pliocene man of Foxhall in East Anglia," *Natural History* 21, 567.

29. Moir, "Tertiary Man in England," *Natural History* 24, 647.

30. Nilsson, *The Pleistocene,* 106.

31. Ragazzoni, *"La collina di Castenedolo, solto il rapporto antropologico, geologico ed agronomico," Commentari dell Ateneo di Brescia,* 120–128. Quoted passages translated by Michael A. Cremo.

32. Harland et al., *A Geologic Time Scale,* 110.

33. Barker et al., "British Museum Natural Radiocarbon Measurements VII," *Radiocarbon* 13, 157–188.

34. de Mortillet, *Le Préhistorique,* 70. Quoted passages translated by Michael A. Cremo.

35. Issel, "Résumé des recherches concernant l'ancienneté de l'homme en Ligurie," *Congrès International d'Anthropologie et d'Archéologie Préhistoriques, Paris 1867, Compte Rendu,* 75–89.

36. de Mortillet, opus cit.

37. Deo Gratias, "Sur l'homme tertiaire de Savone," *Congrès International*

d'Anthropologie et d'Archéologie Préhistoriques, Bologna 1871, Compte Rendu, 419–420. Quoted passages translated by Michael A. Cremo.

38. Winslow, "The President Reads Extracts From a Letter From Dr. C. F. Winslow Relating the Discovery of Human Remains in Table Mountain, Cal. (Jan 1)," *Proceedings of the Boston Society of Natural History* 15, 257–58.

39. Slemmons, opus cit. 200.

40. 1862, 470.

41. July 9, 1985.

Chapter 10   The Fine-tuned Universe

1. Boulding, "Science: Our Common Heritage," 834.

2. Most of the discussion in this chapter has been adapted from the chapter, "A Universe Designed for Life" found in Cremo, *Human Devolution*, 463–481.

3. Rees, *Just Six Numbers: The Deep Forces That Shape the Universe*, 31.

4. Ibid, 115.

5. Ibid.

6. Ibid.

7. Ibid, 113–114.

8. Barrow and Tipler, *The Anthropic Cosmological Principle*, 22.

Chapter 11
Consciousness, Near-death Experiences, and Reincarnation

1. I should mention that the point of this example is not that the world is as unreal as a dream. The world exists (although it may in some ways be something else than we often take it to be). The waking state is also, of course, a higher state of reality than the dreaming state. This is clear by the fact that in the waking state we can both understand and analyze our dreams, but the reverse does not hold true. The only point of my example here is to draw attention to the unchanging nature of the conscious self.

2. *Bhagavad-gita* 2.13ff. See Bhaktivedanta Swami Prabhupada, *Bhagavad-gita As It Is*, 91ff.

3. Phaedo 78b-c and 79d-e. Here taken from Hamilton, *The Collected Dialogues of Plato*, 62–63.

4. Fodor, "The Big Idea: Can There Be a Science of Mind?", 5.

5. Quoted from Humphrey, *Consciousness: the Achilles Heel of Darwinism? Thank God, Not Quite*, 50–64.

6. Ibid.

7. Chalmers, "Consciousness and its Place in Nature."

8. Wigner, *Two Kinds of Reality*, 250.

9. Eddington, *Science and the Unseen World*. Here quoted from Webb, *Darwin's Secret Identity*, 101.

10. Eddington, *The Philosophy of Physical Science*, 95. Here quoted from Webb, *Darwin's Secret Identity*, 101.

11. Huxley, *Essays Upon Some Controverted Questions*, 220.

12. Rensch, *Evolution Above the Species Level*, 355.

13. Popper and Eccles, *The Self and Its Brain*, 362.

14. For more details on Pam Reynolds, see Beauregard and O'Leary, *The Spiritual Brain*, 153–155.

15. Sabom, *Recollections of Death: A Medical Investigation*, 9–10.

16. Ibid., 10.

17. Ibid., 33.

18. Ibid., 64–67.

19. Ibid., 83–87.

20. van Lommel, *Continuity of Our Consciousness*, 115–132. Here adapted from Beauregard and O'Leary, *The Spiritual Brain* (see footnote 13), 156–157.

21. Ibid., *The Spiritual Brain*, 155.

22. Sabom, *Recollections of Death*, 186.

23. Stevenson, "Birthmarks and Birth Defects Corresponding to Wounds on Deceased Persons," 403.

24. Shroder, "A Matter of Death and Life: Ian Stevenson's Scientific Search for Evidence of Reincarnation."

25. Stevenson, *Twenty Cases Suggestive of Reincarnation*, 52–67.

26. Stevenson, *Where Reincarnation and Biology Intersect*, 49–51.

27. Griffin, *Parapsychology, Philosophy and Spirituality: A Postmodern Exploration*, 193–194; here adapted from Cremo, *Human Devolution*, 229.

28. Shroder, "A Matter of Death and Life: Ian Stevenson's Scientific Search for Evidence of Reincarnation."

29. Stevenson, *Where Reincarnation and Biology Intersect*, 186–187.

Chapter 12   The Scientific Aspect of the Supernatural

1. Poll showing that a majority of people believe in the paranormal can be found at www.gallup.com/poll/16915/Three-Four-Americans-Believe-Paranormal.aspx.

2. Radin and Nelson, "Evidence for Consciousness-related Anomalies in Random Physical Systems," 1499–1514.

3. Radin, *The Conscious Universe: The Scientific Truth of Psychic Phenomena*, 2. Here quoted from Beauregard and O'Leary, *The Spiritual Brain*, 168.

4. Hurwic, *Pierre Curie*, 264. Quoted from Cremo, *Human Devolution*, 163.
5. Ibid., *Human Devolution*, 162–163.
6. Ibid., 163–164.
7. Charles Darwin to A. R. Wallace, 27 March 1869, *More Letters of Charles Darwin*, vol. 1, 312.
8. Wallace, *Miracles and Modern Spiritualism*, 127–128.
9. Wallace, *Miracles and Modern Spiritualism*, 127–128.
10. Ibid., *x*.
11. The segment on Rupert Sheldrake has been adapted from Sheldrake and Smart, "A Dog That Seems To Know When His Owner is Coming Home: Videotaped Experiments and Observations," 233–255.
12. Ibid.
13. Adapted with permission from Rupert Sheldrake's homepage at www.sheldrake.org/D&C/controversies/Dawkins.html.
14. Broad and Wade, *Betrayers of the Truth*, 122.
15. Durrani, "Physicists Probe the Paranormal," 5.
16. Cartlidge, "Pioneer of the Paranormal," 10–11.
17. Josephson, "'Beyond Quantum Theory: A Realist Psycho-biological Interpretation of Reality,'" 43–45.
18. Utts and Josephson, "The Paranormal: The Evidence and its Implications for Consciousness," v.

Chapter 13   Inspiration, Instinct, and Superconsciousness

1. Hadamard, *The Psychology of Invention in the Mathematical Field*, 16. Quoted from Thompson, Cremo, and Gordon, *Origins*, 26.
2. Ibid.
3. Poincaré, *The Foundations of Science*, 390.
4. Balázs and István, *Nature's IQ*, 82–83.
5. Ibid., 88–90.
6. Ibid., 91–93.
7. Ibid., 94.
8. Roach, "Internal Clock Leads Monarch Butterflies to Mexico."
9. Poincaré, *The Foundations of Science*, 391.
10. Brute-force problem solving is a general problem-solving technique consisting of systematically enumerating all possible candidates for the solution and checking whether or not each satisfies the problem's statement.

Chapter 14   The Vedic Paradigm

1. Clark and Stearn, *The Geological Evolution of North America*, 43.
2. *Vishnu Purana* 6.7.61.
3. Gould, *Rocks of Ages: Science and Religion in the Fullness of Life*, 539–542.
4. Newton, *Principia*, 544.
5. Agassiz, *Essay on Classification*, 137
6. Darwin, C., *On the Origin of Species*, 445.
7. Gould, *The Panda's Thumb*, 20.
8. Futuyma, *Evolution*, 49.
9. Letter from Charles Darwin to Asa Gray, May 22, 1860.
10. Wallis, "The Evolution Wars," *Time*, August 15, 2005, 27–35.
11. Dawkins, *River Out of Eden*, 133.
12. Bhaktivedanta Swami Prabhupada, *Bhagavad-gita* 8.20.
13. Swami, Suhotra, *Vedanta Psychology*, xi.
14. From a conversation on July 3, 1976, in Washington, D.C.
15. From a lecture in Hawaii given on February 3, 1975.

Glossary

amino acid: a group of simple molecules that serve as building blocks of protein.

amniotes: any of a group of animals that go through embryonic development within an amnion, i.e. reptiles, mammals, and birds.

anthropical principle: the idea that the universe has the precise properties that allow for human life.

Australopithecus: lit., "the southern ape"; a genus of extinct hominins who are said to have lived in Africa 3–4 million years ago.

bacterial flagellum: a tail-like structure found on many bacteria and other unicellular organisms that acts as a propeller to drive the organism forward.

Cambrian: a geological period from about 550–490 million years ago.

camera eye: the complex eye found in vertebrates.

catalysis: a chemical reaction increased or decreased by a catalyst.

catalyst: a substance that speeds up a chemical reaction without being affected by the reaction.

chromosome: cluster of DNA found in the cell's nucleus that carries the genetic information for the organism. Different organisms have different numbers of chromosomes.

cilium (pl. cilia): small hairlike structures extending approximately 5–10 micrometers out from cell bodies.

class: *see* classification.

classification: a system used in biology and invented by the Swedish naturalist Carolus Linnaeus that divides living organisms into kingdoms, phyla, classes, orders, families, genera, and species (which are then subdivided into varieties).

collagen: the main protein component of connective tissue in animals; the most abundant protein in mammals.

common ancestry: the idea that all living organisms have descended from a common ancestor.

complex specified information, specified complexity: an argument proposed by William Dembski to support the theory of intelligent design. The argument refers to the understanding that patterns that are both complex and at the same time match up with another, independently given pattern indicate the involvement of an intelligent cause in their formation.

convergence, convergent evolution: the evolution of similar traits in unrelated species.

creationist: although this word is usually used to define a person who accepts the Biblical account of creation, in its broadest sense it refers to any person who accepts that God had something to do with the creation of life on earth.

cytochrome C: a common protein found in most plants, animals, and unicellular organisms.

Darwinism: Darwin's original theory of evolution. More broadly, any theory of evolution that restricts itself to a mechanism of "natural" causes.

descent with modification: Darwin's original idea that all beings arose by descent from a common ancestor over millions of years through small, gradual changes over each generation.

deuterium: a hydrogen isotope with both a proton and a neutron in the nucleus (most hydrogen atoms have only one proton and no neutron).

DNA: deoxyribonucleic acid, one of the cell's two important nucleic acids; the large molecule that carries all a cell's genetic information.

DNA double helix: the structure of DNA discovered by Francis Crick and James Watson in 1954. The two long, parallel DNA strands entwine around one another in a double spiral (helix).

dynein: a motor protein that converts chemical energy into mechanical energy.

embryology: the science that studies embryonic development.

empirical: relating to knowledge gained through sense perception and experience.

enzyme: a biological molecule that facilitates chemical reactions in living organisms. Almost all enzymes are proteins.

Eocene: a geological period from about 55–38 million years ago.

epiphenomenon: a secondary effect of a primary phenomenon, but one which cannot affect the primary phenomenon.

eukaryote: an organism with a cell nucleus.

family: *see* classification.

fossil: an organism or a part of an organism preserved in the earth from ancient times.

gene: the basic unit of heredity; found in sections of the DNA.

genera, genus: *see* classification.

genetic code: a code that specifies the synthesizing of proteins from DNA.

genetics: the science of heredity.

genome: the full set of all the genetic material found in a cell or organism.

hemoglobin: the oxygen-carrying protein in the blood of vertebrates.

hominins: all humans, great apes, and their supposed common ancestors.

Homo erectus: extinct species of the line supposedly leading to modern humans; said to have existed from about 2 to half a million years ago.

Homo habilis: extinct species of the line supposedly leading to modern humans; said to have existed from about 2.5–1.6 million years ago.

homologous: in evolutionary terms, traits that are related through common ancestry.

hopeful monster: a theory stating that evolution happens not only gradually, as Darwin saw it, but also through sudden leaps, such as by a dinosaur giving birth to a bird.

Intelligent Design, design: the idea that life and nature contain features and events that are best explained by intelligent causes.

intermediate form: an intermediate species between two species.

irreducibly complex system: a system performing a given function and consisting of a number of interrelated parts, in which the absence of any one of those parts would cause the entire system to effectively lose its function.

kingdom: *see* classification.

lateral gene transfer: also called horizontal gene transfer; any process by which genetic material is transferred from organism A to organism B, in which B is not the offspring of A.

marsupial: a class of mammals in which females carry their young in a pouch (*marsupium*). Mainly found in Australia.

mesmerism: a healing process using supposed magnetic fluids in the body; succeeded by hypnotism.

metabolism: the chemical reactions that maintain life in living organisms.

Mesozoic: a geological era from about 248–65 million years ago. Includes the Triassic, Jurassic, and Cretaceous periods.

microtubule: a protein that is part of the structural components of cells.

mitochondrion (pl. mitochondria): an organelle found in most eucaryotic cells. A mitochondrion generates energy in the cell and contains its own DNA.

Modern Synthesis: see Neo-Darwinism.

monomer: a small molecule that can combine with other monomers to form a polymer.

mutation: any sudden change, from parent to offspring, in a heredi-tary trait – for instance, a change in the sequence of nucleotides in the genes.

natural evolution: evolution without unnatural, or supernatural, mediation.

natural selection: nature's own process of elimination or selection by which favorable traits become more common through the genera-tions of a population and unfavorable traits become less common. Individuals with less favorable traits for survival are less prone to pass on their genes, which causes these traits to gradually be eliminated from the gene pool.

NDE: near-death experience.

Neo-Darwinism: a theory combining Darwin's idea of common descent and natural selection with Mendel's theory of genetics.

nucleic acids: *see* DNA and RNA.

nucleotides, or nucleotide bases: the molecules in DNA and RNA (adenine, cytosine, guanine, thymine, and uracil) whose sequence spells out the genetic code.

order: *see* classification.

Ordovician: a geological period from about 490–438 million years ago.

organelle: an "organ" within a cell.

paleoanthropology: the study of ancient humans through fossils.

paleontology: the study of the past geological periods as they are known through fossils.

pangenesis: Darwin's (and Lamarck's) theory of the inheritance of acquired traits.

parapsychology: the study of paranormal psychological phenomena.

phosphates: a group of inorganic salts derived from phosphoric acid.

phylogenetic tree: a map of relatedness between species. Darwin expected such phylogenies to reflect evolution and to resemble trees, with one species at the root and more species gradually branching off along the trunk.

phylogeny: the study of relatedness among various groups of organisms.

phylum (pl. phyla): *see* classification.

placental: a mammal having a placenta.

polymer: a large molecule that consists of a repetition of monomers.

polynucleotide: an organic polymer, such as DNA or RNA, composed of nucleotides bonded in a chain.

prebiotic: relating to the chemicals or the environment before the beginning of cellular life as we know it.

Precambrian: the geological periods before the Cambrian (about 550 million years ago).

prokaryote: a unicellular organism that lacks a cell nucleus.

protein: an organic polymer made of amino acids linked in a chain and joined by peptide bonds.

proteomics: the large-scale study of proteins.

punctuated equilibrium: a theory stating that evolution is characterized by long periods of stasis interrupted by sudden and very drastic developments of new species within a very small, isolated number of individuals.

reducing atmosphere: an atmosphere devoid of oxygen.

ribosome: the organelle where the assembling of proteins from amino acids takes place.

RNA: ribonucleic acid. One of the cell's two important nucleic acids. RNA functions, among other things, as the intermediate between DNA and proteins.

RNA world: the theory that RNA was the first large biomolecule to evolve.

special creation: the idea that all species were created separately (often associated with biblical creation). Darwin argued for natural evolution as opposed to special creation.

speciation: the formation of a new species.

species: *see* classification.

sugar: a molecular group of simple carbohydrates that are essential to many processes in living organisms.

taxon: a category in a classification system. *See* classification.

taxonomy: *see* classification.

telekinesis: the process of moving physical objects through mental power.

telepathy: the process of transferring thoughts and/or feelings from one person to another without any physical or sensual mechanism.

therapod: a suborder of dinosaurs.

therapsid: an order of animals consisting of all mammals and their assumed evolutionary ancestors.

transitional: intermediate.

variety: *see* classification.

vertebrate: an animal with a backbone or spinal column; the vertebrate phylum.

Bibliography

A relic of a by-gone age, *Scientific American*, 7, 38 (June 5, 1852), 298.

Adoutte, André et al., "The New Animal Phylogeny: Reliability and Implications," Proceedings of the National Academy of Sciences, USA, 97 (2000), 4453–4456.

Agassiz, Louis, *Essay on Classification*, Cambridge: Harvard University Press, 1962 [originally from 1857].

Aguinaldo, Anna Marie A. et al., "Evidence for A Clade of Nematodes, Arthropods, and Embryos: New Perspectives on the Cambrian Explosion," *Nature*, 387 (1997), 489–93.

Aizawa, S. I. Flagellar, "Assembly in Salmonella Typhimurium," *Molecular Microbiology*, 19 (1996), 1–5.

Alberts, B., "The Cell as a Collection of Protein Machines: Preparing the Next Generation of Molecular Biologists," *Cell*, 92 (1998), 291–294.

Anderson, E., "Who's Who in the Pleistocene: A Mammalian Bestiary," In Martin, P. S., and Klein, R. G., eds. *Quaternary Extinctions*. Tucson: University of Arizona Press, 1984.

Ankel-Simons, Friderun, and Cummins, Jim M., "Misconceptions About Mitochondria and Mammalian Fertilization: Implications for Theories on Human Evolution," *Proceedings of the National Academy of Sciences*, 93, 24 (November 26, 1996), 13859–13863.

Atkins, P. W., "Review of Michael Behe's *Darwin's Black Box*," *www.infidels.org/library/modern/peter_atkins/behe.html*. 1998.

Ayala, Francisco J., "Darwin's Greatest Discovery: Design Without Designer," *Proceedings of the National Academy of Sciences*, 104 (May 15, 2007), 8567–8573.

Barker, H., Burleigh, R., and Meeks, N., "British Museum Natural Radiocarbon Measurements VII," *Radiocarbon*, 13 (1971), 157–188.

Barrow, John, and Tipler, Frank, *The Cosmological Anthropic Principle,* Oxford University Press, 1996.

Beauregard, Mario, and O'Leary, Denyse, *The Spiritual Brain,* New York: HarperOne 2007.

Behe, M. J., *Darwin's Black Box: The Biochemical Challenge to Evolution,* New York: The Free Press, 1996.

Behe, M. J., "Reply to My Critics: A Response to Reviews of *Darwin's Black Box: The Biochemical Challenge to Evolution,*" *Biology and Philosophy,* 16 (2000), 685–709.

Behe, Michael J., *The Edge of Evolution: The Search for the Limits of Darwinism,* New York: Free Press, 2008.

Berra, Tim, *Evolution and the Myth of Creationism,* Palo Alto, CA, USA: Stanford University Press, 1990.

Bhaktivedanta Swami Prabhupada, A. C., *Sri Caitanya-caritamrta,* Adi-Lila, Volume 3, Los Angeles: The Bhaktivedanta Book Trust, 1974.

Bhaktivedanta Swami Prabhupada, A. C., lecture on *Bhagavad-gita,* text 16.7. Hawaii (February 3, 1975).

Bhaktivedanta Swami Prabhupada, A. C., *Life Comes from Life,* Los Angeles: The Bhaktivedanta Book Trust, 1979.

Bhaktivedanta Swami Prabhupada, A. C., *Bhagavad-gita As It Is,* Sydney: The Bhaktivedanta Book Trust, 1986.

Blair, Jaime E. et al., "The Evolutionary Position of Nematodes," *Biomed Central Evolutionary Biology,* 2 (2002), 7.

Boisvert, Catherine A., Mark-Kurik, Elga, and Ahlberg, Per E., "The Pectoral Fin of Panderichthys and the Origin of Digits," *Nature,* 456 (December 4, 2008), 636–638.

Boulding, Kenneth R., "Our Common Heritage," *Science,* 207 (February 22, 1980), 834.

Boxhorn, Joseph, "Observed Instances of Speciation," *The TalkOrigins Archive.* See online at http://www.toarchive.org/faqs/faq-speciation.html.

Brooks, J., and Shaw, G., *Origin and Development of Living Systems,* London and New York: Academic Press, 1973.

Bugge, T. H., Flick, M. J., Daugherty, C. C., and Degen, J. L., "Plasminogen Deficiency Causes Severe Thrombosis but is Compatible with Development and Reproduction," *Genes and Development,* 9 (1995), 794–807.

Bugge, T. H., Kombrinck, K. W., Flick, M. J., Daugherty, C. C., Danton, M. J., and Degen, J. L., "Loss of Fibrinogen Rescues Mice from the Pleiotropic Effects of Plasminogen Deficiency," *Cell,* 87 (1996), 709–719.

Bugge,T.H., Xiao, Q., Kombrinck, K. W., Flick, M. J., Holmback, K., Danton, M. J., Colbert, M. C., Witte, D. P., Fujikawa, K., Davie, E. W., & Degen, J. L., "Fatal Embryonic Bleeding Events in Mice Lacking Tissue Factor, The Cell- Associated

Initiator of Blood Coagulation," *Proceedings of the National Academy of Sciences of the United States of America*, 93 (1996), 6258–6263.

Campbell, Neil A., and Reece, Jane B., *Biology* (International Edition), San Francisco: Pearson Education Inc., 2005.

Cann, R. L., Stoneking, M., and Wilson, A. C., "Mitocondrial DNA and Human Evolution," *Nature*, 325 (1987), 31–36.

Cartlidge, Edwin, "Pioneer of the Paranormal," *Physics World* (May 2002), 10–11. Online at http://www.tcm.phy.cam.ac.uk/~bdj10/mm/articles/PWprofile.html.

Cavalier-Smith,T., "The Blind Biochemist," *Trends in Ecology and Evolution*, 12 (1997), 162–163.

Chalmers, David, "Consciousness and its Place in Nature," *Philosophy of Mind: Classical and Contemporary Readings*, Oxford 2002, see also http://consc.net/papers/nature.pdf.

Chanda, Sunirmal, "Amiya Kumar Ghosh" (obituary), *Science and Culture*, 51, 8 (August 1985), 266–267. Also available online at http://www.palynology.org/history/ghoshak.html.

Chavaillon, J., Chavaillon, N., Coppens, Y., and Senut, B., "Présence d'hominidé dans le site oldowayen de Gomboré I à Melka Kunturé, Éthiopie," *Comptes Rendus de l'Académie des Sciences, Series D*, 285 (1977), 961–963.

Clark, Thomas H., and Stearn, Colin W., *The Geological Evolution of North America*, New York: Ronald Press, 1960.

Coyne, J. A., "God in the Details," *Nature*, 383 (1996), 227–228.

Cremo, M. A., *Forbidden Archeology's Impact*. Los Angeles: Bhaktivedanta Book Publishing, 1998.

Cremo, M. A., and Thompson, R. L., *Forbidden Archeology*. First edition revised. Los Angeles: Bhaktivedanta Book Publishing, 1998.

Cremo, Michael, "Paleobotanical Anomalies Bearing on the Age of the Salt Range Formation of Pakistan: A Historical Survey of an Unresolved Scientific Controversy," a paper for Presentation at XXI International Congress of History of Science, Mexico City, July 8–14, 2001.

Cremo, Michael, *Human Devolution*, Los Angeles: Bhaktivedanta Book Trust, 2003.

Daeschler et al., "A Devonian tetrapod-like fish and the evolution of the tetrapod body plan," *Nature*, 440 (April 6, 2006), 757–763.

Darwin, Charles R., "Letter to Asa Gray, May 22, 1860." See online at http://www.darwinproject.ac.uk/darwinletters/calendar/entry-2814.html.

Darwin, F., *The Life and Letters of Charles Darwin*, vol. 1, London: John Murray, 1888.

Darwin, F., *The Life and Letters of Charles Darwin*, vol. 2, London: John Murray, 1888.

Darwin, Charles, "Charles Darwin to A. R. Wallace, 27 March 1869," in Darwin,

Francis, and Seward, A. C. (eds.), *More Letters of Charles Darwin*, vol. 1, London: John Murray, 1903.

Darwin, Charles R., *The Voyage of the Beagle*, London: J. M. Dent, 1959.

Darwin, Charles R., *The Origin of Species by Means of Natural Selection: or The Preservation of Favoured Races in the Struggle for Life*, First Edition. Penguin: London, 1985.

Darwin, Charles R., *The Origin of Species*, New York: Bantam Books, 1999.

Dawkins, Richard, *The Blind Watchmaker*, New York: W. W. Norton & Company, Inc., 1986.

Dawkins, Richard, *River Out of Eden: A Darwinian View of Life*, BasicBooks 2005, 133.

Dawson, Albert, From an interview printed in *The Christian Commonwealth*, December 10, 1903.

Day, M. H., and Molleson, T. I., "The Trinil Femora," *Symposia of the Society for the Study of Human Biology*, 2 (1973), 127–154.

De Mortillet, G., *Le Préhistorique*, Paris: C. Reinwald, 1883. Quoted passages translated by Michael A. Cremo.

De Vries, Hugo, *The Mutation Theory*, Vol. II, Chicago: Open Court, 1919.

Dembski, William A., and Wells, Jonathan, *The Design of Life: Discovering Signs of Intelligence in Biological Systems*, Dallas, TX, USA: Foundation for Thoughts and Ethics, 2007.

Denton, Michael, *Evolution, a Theory in Crisis*, Bethesda, MD, USA: Adler & Adler, 1985.

Deo Gratias, Rev. [D. Perrando], "Sur l'homme tertiaire de Savone," *Congrès International d'Anthropologie et d'Archéologie Préhistoriques, Bologna 1871, Compte Rendu* (1873), 417–420. Quoted passages translated by Michael A. Cremo.

DeRosier, D. J., "The Turn of the Screw: The Bacterial Flagellar Motor," *Cell*, 93 (1998), 17–20.

Dickerson, Richard E., "The Game of Science," *Journal of Molecular Evolution*, 34 (1992), 277–279.

Dobzhansky, Theodosius, "Nothing in Biology Makes Sense Except in the Light of Evolution," *The American Biology Teacher*, 35 (March 1973), 125–129.

Doolittle, R. F., "A Delicate Balance," *Boston Review* (Feb./March 1997), 28–29.

Doolittle, W. Ford, "Uprooting the Tree of Life," *Scientific American*, 282 (February 2000), 90–95.

Dorit, R., "Molecular Evolution and Scientific Inquiry, Misperceived," *American Scientist*, 85 (1997), 474–475.

Durrani, Matin, "Physicists Probe the Paranormal," *Physics World* (May 2000), 5. Online at http://physicsworld.com/cws/article/print/652.

Dutcher, S. K., "Flagellar Assembly in Two Hundred and Fifty Easy-to-follow Steps," *Trends in Genetics*, 11 (1995), 398–404.

Eddington, Arthur S., *Science and the Unseen World*, London: George Allen and Unwin Ltd., 1929.

Eddington, Arthur S., *The Philosophy of Physical Science*, Cambridge: Cambridge University Press, 1939.

Eldredge, Niles, *Reinventing Darwin: The Great Debate at the High Table of Evolutionary Theory*, New York: John Wiley & Sons, 1995.

Feduccia, Alan, Lingham-Soliar, Theagarten and Hinchcliffe, J. Richard, "Exist? Testing the Hypothesis on Neontological and Paleontological Evidence," *Journal of Morphology*, 266, 2 (2005), 125–166.

"Fish-o-pod 'Missing Link' Discovered: Media Goes Nuts," April 6, 2006. See online: http://www.creationsafaris.com/crev200604.htm#fossil201.

Fodor, Jerry A., "The Big Idea. Can There be a Science of Mind?", *Times Literary Supplement*, 1 (July 3 and 5, 1992).

Futuyma, Douglas, *Science on Trial: The Case for Evolution*, New York: Pantheon, 1982.

Futuyma, Douglas, *Evolutionary Biology, 3rd edition*, Sunderland, Mass., USA: Sinnauer, 1998.

Futuyma, Douglas, J., *Evolution*, Sunderland, Mass., USA: Sinauer Associates, 2005.

Gates, Bill, *The Road Ahead*, London: Penguin, 1995, Revised 1996.

Gavin, A.C., Bosche, M., Krause, R., Grandi, P., Marzioch, M., Bauer, A., Schultz, J., Rick, J. M., Michon, A. M., Cruciat, C. M., Remor, M., Hofert, C., Schelder, M., Brajenovic, M., Ruffner, H., Merino, A., Klein, K., Hudak, M., Dickson, D., Rudi, T., Gnau, V., Bauch, A., Bastuck, S., Huhse, B., Leutwein, C., Heurtier, M. A., Copley, R. R., Edelmann, A., Querfurth, E., Rybin, V., Drewes, G., Raida, M., Bouwmeester, T., Bork, P., Seraphin, B., Kuster, B., Neubauer, G., and Superti-Furga, G., "Functional Organization of the Yeast Proteome by Systematic Analysis of Protein Complexes," *Nature*, 415 (2002), 141–147.

Gibbons, Ann, "Modern Men Trace Ancestry to African Migrants," *Science* 292 (2001), 1052.

Gould, Stephen Jay, *The Panda's Thumb*, New York: W. W. Norton & Co., 1980.

Gould, Stephen Jay, "Rocks of Ages: Science and Religion in the Fullness of Life," *Science, Technology, & Human Values*, Vol. 27, No. 4 (Autumn, 2002), 539–542.

Greenspan, N. S., "Not-So-Intelligent Design," *The Scientist* 16 (2002), 12.

Griffin, David Ray, *Parapsychology, Philosophy and Spirituality: A Postmodern Exploration*, Albany, NY: State University of New York Press, 1997.

Hadamard, Jacques, *The Psychology of Invention in the Mathematical Field*, Princeton: Princeton University Press, 1949.

Halkier, T., *Mechanisms in blood coagulation fibrinolysis and the complement system*. Cambridge: Cambridge University Press, 1992.

Hamilton, Edith, ed. Phaedo 78b-c and 79d-e, *The Collected Dialogues of Plato*, Princeton: Princeton University Press, 16th printing, 1996.

Harding, L., "History of Modern Man Unravels as German Scholar is Exposed as Fraud," *The Guardian* (February 19, 2005), 3, "Life News and Features" section.

Harland, W. B., Cox, A. V., Llewellyn, P. G., Pickton, C. A. G., Smith, A. G., and Walters, R., *A Geologic Time Scale*, Cambridge: Cambridge University Press, 1982.

Harold, F. M., *The Way of the Cell*, Oxford: Oxford University Press, 2001.

Heribert-Nilsson, N., *Synthetische Artbildung*, Gleerup, Sweden: Lund University, 1954.

Highfield, Roger, "Bald Truth About Dinosaur Feathers," *The Daily Telegraph*, (January 9, 2008).

Hitching, Francis, *The Neck of the Giraffe*, New Haven, Connecticut, USA: Ticknor & Fields, 1982.

Holmes, W. H., (1899) "Review of the Evidence Relating to Auriferous Gravel Man in California," *Smithsonian Institution Annual Report 1898–1899*, pp. 419–472.

Horgan, J., "In the Beginning …," *Scientific American*, Vol. 264 (2 February 1991), 100–109.

Hornyánszky, Balázs, and Tasi, István, *Nature's IQ*, Badger, CA, USA: Torchlight Publishing, 2009.

Humphrey, Nicholas, "Consciousness: the Achilles Heel of Darwinism? Thank God, Not Quite," *Intelligent Thought: Science Versus the Intelligent Design Movement*, edited by John Brockmann, New York: Vintage, 2006, 50–64. Also available online at: http://www.humphrey.org.uk/papers/2006Consciousness.pdf.

Hueck, C. J., "Type III Protein Secretion Systems in Bacterial Pathogens of Animals and Plants," *Microbiology and Molecular Biology Reviews* 62 (1998), 379–433.

Hurwic, Anna, *Pierre Curie*, Paris: Flammarion, 1995.

Huxley, T. H., *Essays Upon Some Controverted Questions*, London: Macmillan & Co., 1892.

Hrdlicka, A., *Early Man in South America*. Washington, D. C.: Smithsonian Institution, 1912.

Issel, A., "Résumé des Recherches Concernant L'ancienneté de L'homme en Ligurie," *Congrès International d'Anthropologie et d'Archéologie Préhistoriques, Paris 1867, Compte Rendu* (1868), 75–89.

Jacob, T., Palaeoanthropological discoveries in Indonesia with special reference to finds of the last two decades. *Journal of Human Evolution* 2 (1973), 473–485.

Johanson, D. C., Masao, F. T., Eck, G. G., White, T. D., Walter, R. C., Kimbel, W. H.,

Asfaw, B., Manega, P., Ndessokia, P., and Suwa, G., "New Partial Skeleton of *Homo Habilis* from Olduvai Gorge, Tanzania," *Nature, 327* (1987), 205–209.

Johnson, Phillip, *Darwin on Trial,* Second Edition, Downers Grove, Illinois, USA: InterVarsity Press, 1993.

Jones, Do-While, "The Many Myths of Evolution," (May 1997). See online: http://www.ridgenet.net/~do_while/sage/v11i8f.htm.

Jones, Martin, and Blaxter, Mark, "Animal Roots and Shoots," *Nature, 434* (2005), 1076–77.

Josephson, Brian, " 'Beyond Quantum Theory: A Realist Psycho-biological Interpretation of Reality' Revisited," *Biosystems, 64* (1–3), (Jan. 2002), 43–45. Also online at http://arxiv.org/ftp/quant-ph/papers/0105/0105027.pdf.

Joyce, Gerald, "The Antiquity of RNA-based Evolution," *Nature 418* (2002), 215.

Joyce, G., and Orgel, L., *The RNA World, Second Edition*, Cold Spring Harbor, N.Y.: Cold Spring Harbor Laboratory Press, 1999.

Kauffman, S. A., *At Home in the Universe: The Search for Laws of Self-Organization and Complexity*, New York: Oxford University Press, 1995.

Lake, James A., et al., "Mix and Match in the Tree of Life," *Science, 283* (1999), 2027–28.

Leclercq, S., "Evidence of Vascular Plants in the Cambrian," *Evolution, X,* 2 (June 1956), 109–114.

Leakey, M. D., "Footprints in the Ashes of Time," *National Geographic, 155* (1979), 446–457.

Leakey, R. E., "Skull 1470," *National Geographic, 143* (1973), 819–829.

Lingham-Soliar, Theagarten, "A Unique Cross Section Through the Skin of the Dinosaur Psittacosaurus from China Showing a Complex Fibre Architecture," *Proceedings of the Royal Society, Biological Science, 275,* 1636 (April 2008), 775–780. Online at http://rspb.royalsocietypublishing.org/content/275/1636/775.full.

Lynch, Michael, "The Age and Relationships of the Major Animal Phyla," *Evolution, 53,* 2 (April 1999), 319–25. Online at http://www.indiana.edu/~lynchlab/PDF/Lynch90.pdf.

Macbeth, Norman, *Darwin Retried*. Boston: Gambit, 1971.

Mackie, Samuel Joseph, ed., "Fossil Man," *The Geologist, 5* (1862), 470.

Marshall, L. G., Webb, S. D., Sepkoski, Jr., J. J., and Raup, D. M., Mammalian evolution and the great American interchange. *Science, 215* (1982), 1351–1357.

Martin, Larry D., and Czerkas, Stephan A., "The Fossil Record of Feather Evolution in the Mesozoic," *American Zoologist, 40,* 4 (2000), 687.

Mayr's speech freely available on the Internet (as of June 2008) at: http://www.biologie.uni-hamburg.de/b-online/e36_2/darwin_influence.htm.

McCrone, John, "Power of the Paranormal: Why it Won't Surrender to Science," *New Scientist* (March 13–19, 2004).

Mendel, Gregor Johann, "Versuche über Pflanzen-Hybriden," originally published by Verh. Naturforsch. *Ver. Brünn*, 4 (1866) 3–47. Available in English on the Internet at http://www.mendelweb.org/Mendel.html.

Miller, K. R., *Finding Darwin's God: A Scientist's Search for Common Ground between God and Evolution*, New York: Cliff Street Books, 1999.

Moore, David W., "Three in Four Americans Believe in the Paranormal" (June 16, 2005). See online at http://www.gallup.com/poll/16915/Three-Four-Americans-Believe-Paranormal.aspx.

Morris, Simon Conway, *Life's Solution, Inevitable Humans in a Lonely Universe*, Cambridge: Cambridge University Press, 2003.

National Academy of Sciences, *Science, Evolution and Creationism*, Washington, DC: National Academies Press, 2008. Free online access at http://www.nap.edu/catalog.php?record_id=11876.

Newton, Sir Isaac, *Principia*, Berkeley, CA, USA: University of California Press, 1966.

Nilsson, T., *The Pleistocene*. Dordrecht, D. Reidel, 1983.

Nishimura, Yoshiki et al., "Active digestion of sperm mitochondrial DNA in single living sperm revealed by optical tweezers," *Proceedings of the National Academy of Sciences* USA, 2006 January 31; 103(5), 1382–1387.

Orgel, Leslie E., "The Implausibility of Metabolic Cycles on the Prebiotic Earth," *Public Library of Science: Biology*, 6(1), e18, Jan 22, 2008, doi:10.1371/journal.pbio.0060018.

Osborn, H. F., "The Pliocene Man of Foxhall in East Anglia," *Natural History*, 21 (1921), 565–576.

Patterson, B., and Howells, W. W., "Hominid humeral fragment from Early Pleistocene of northwestern Kenya," *Science*, 15 (1967), 64–66.

Patterson, Colin, *Evolution*, Ithaca, NY, USA: Cornell University Press (First Edition, 1978, or Second Edition, 1999).

Philippe, Hervé, and Forterre, Patrick, "The Rooting of the Universal Tree of Life Is Not Reliable," *Journal of Molecular Evolution*, 49 (1999), 509–523.

Philippe, Hervé, and Forterre, Patrick, "Where Is the Root of the Universal Tree of Life," *BioEssays* 21 (1999), 871–79.

Philippe, Hervé et al., "Multigene Analysis of Bilaterian Animals Corroborate the Monophyly of Ecdysozoa, Lophotrochozoa, and Protostomia," *Molecular Biology and Evolution*, 22 (2005), 1246–53.

Poincaré, Henri, *The Foundations of Science*, Lancaster, Pennsylvania, USA: The Science Press, 1946.

Polanyi, Michael, "Life Transcending Physics and Chemistry," *Chemical and Engineering News* (August 21, 1967), 62.

Pomerol, Charles, *Geology of France*, Paris: Masson, 1980.

Pomiankowski, A., "The God of the Tiny Gaps," *New Scientist*, Sept 14, 1996, 44–45.

Protsch, R., "The Age and Stratigraphic Position of Olduvai Hominid I," *Journal of Human Evolution*, 3 (1974), 379–385.

Prum, Richard, "Are Current Critiques of the Therapod Origin of Birds Science? Rebuttal to Feduccia (2002)," *The Auk*, 120, 2 (April 2003), 550–561.

Radin, Dean L., and Nelson, Roger D., "Evidence for Consciousness-related Anomalies in Random Physical Systems," *Foundations of Physics*, 19 (1989), 1499–1514.

Radin, Dean, *The Conscious Universe: The Scientific Truth of Psychic Phenomena*, San Francisco: Harper, 2007.

Ragazzoni, G., "La Collina di Castenedolo, Solto il Rapporto Antropologico, Geologico ed Agronomico," *Commentari dell Ateneo di Brescia* (April 4, 1880), 120–128. Quoted passages translated by Michael A. Cremo.

Raup, David, "Conflicts Between Darwin and Paleontology," *Field Museum of Natural History Bulletin*, 50 (January 1979). See http://www.fossilmuseum.net/Tree_of_Life/Stromatolites.htm.

Rees, Sir Martin, *Just Six Numbers: The Deep Forces That Shape the Universe*, New York: Basic Books, 2000.

Rehbock, Philip F., "Huxley, Haeckel, and the Oceanographers: The Case of Bathybius haeckelii," *Isis*, 66, 4 (Dec. 1975), 504–533.

ReMine, Walter, "Evidence for Message Theory," *Journal of Creation* 20(2), 2006. Also available at the Internet (as of January 2009) at www.creationontheweb.com/images/pdfs/tj/j20_2/j20_2_29-35.pdf.

Roach, John, "Internal Clock Leads Monarch Butterflies to Mexico," *National Geographic*, June 10, 2003.

Rokas, Antonis, et al., "Animal Evolution and the Molecular Signature of Radiations Compressed in Time," *Science* 310 (2005), 1933–38.

Ruse, M., Answering the creationists: Where They Go Wrong and What They're Afraid Of. *Free Inquiry* (March 22, 1998), 28.

Sabom, Michael B., *Recollections of Death: A Medical Investigation*, New York, Harper & Row, 1982.

Sagan, Carl, *Cosmos* (TV series), Los Angeles: KCET, 1979.

Sagan, Carl, *Cosmos*, New York: Random House, 2002.

Semi Creation, *Time* magazine, May 25, 1953.

Shapiro, J., "In the details ... what?" *National Review* (Sept. 16, 1996), 62–65.

Shapiro, L., "The Bacterial Flagellum: From Genetic Network to Complex Architecture. *Cell*, 80 (1995), 525–527.

Shapiro, R. A., "Simpler Origin for Life," *Scientific American* (February 2007). Also available online at http://www.sciam.com/article.cfm?id=a-simpler-origin-for-life&print=true.

Sheldrake, Rupert, http://www.sheldrake.org:80/D&C/controversies/Dawkins.html.

Sheldrake, Rupert, and Smart, Pamela, "A Dog That Seems to Know When His Owner is Coming Home: Videotaped Experiments and Observations," *Journal of Scientific Exploration*, 14 (2000), 233–255. Also available online at http://www.sheldrake.org/Articles&Papers/papers/animals/pdf/dog_video.pdf.

Shipman, Pat, "Birds Do It ... Did Dinosaurs?", *New Scientist* (February 1, 1997), 28.

Shroder, Tom, "A Matter of Death and Life: Ian Stevenson's Scientific Search for Evidence of Reincarnation," *Washington Post Magazine* (August 8, 1999). Available online at: http://www.childpastlives.org/library_articles/oldsouls.htm.

Silliman, Benjamin, "Curious Geological Facts," *American Journal of Science and Arts*, 2 (1820), 144–146.

Slemmons, D. B., "Cenozoic Volcanism of the Central Sierra Nevada, California," *Bulletin of the California Division of Mines and Geology*, 190 (1966), 199–208.

Smith, John Maynard, "Taking a Chance on Evolution," *New York Review of Books* (May 14, 1992), 34–36.

Stainforth, R. M., "Occurrence of Pollen and Spores in the Roraima Formation of Venezuela and British Guiana," *Nature*, 210, 5033 (April 16, 1966), 292–294.

Spinoza, Baruch, *Ethica in Opera quotquae reperta sunt* [1677], 3rd edition, van Vloten, J., and Land, J. P. N., eds., Den Haag, Netherlands: 1914.

Stapp, Henry P., *A Report on the Gaudiya Vaishnava Vedanta Form of Vedic Ontology*, Berkeley: Bhaktivedanta Institute, 1994.

Steen-McIntyre, V., Fryxell, R., and Malde, H. E., "Geologic Evidence for Age of Deposits at Hueyatlaco Archaeological Site, Valsequillo, Mexico," *Quaternary Research*, 16 (1981), 1–17.

Stevenson, Ian, *Twenty Cases Suggestive of Reincarnation*, Charlottesville, VA, USA: University of Virginia Press, 1966, second revised and enlarged edition, 1974.

Stevenson, Ian, "Birthmarks and Birth Defects Corresponding to Wounds on Deceased Persons," *Journal of Scientific Exploration*, 7 (1993), 403–410. Available online at: http://www.childpastlives.org/library_articles/birthmark.htm.

Stevenson, Ian, *Reincarnation and Biology: A Contribution to the Etiology of Birthmarks and Birth Defects*, Westport, Conn., USA: Praeger Publishers, 1997.

Stevenson, Ian, *Where Reincarnation and Biology Intersect*, Westport, Conn., USA: Praeger Publishers, 1997.

Swami, Suhotra, *Vedanta Psychology*, Mayapur, WB, India: The Bhaktivedanta Academy, 2007.

Suh, T. T., Holmback, K., Jensen, N. J., Daugherty, C. C., Small, K., Simon, D. I.,

Potter, S., and Degen, J. L., "Resolution of Spontaneous Bleeding Events but Failure of Pregnancy in Fibrinogen-deficient Mice," *Genes and Development,* 9 (1995), 2020–2033.

Sun, W. Y., Witte, D. P., Degen, J. L., Colbert, M. C., Burkart, M. C., Holmback, K., Xiao, Q., Bugge, T. H., and Degen, S. J., "Prothrombin Deficiency Results in Embryonic and Neonatal Lethality in Mice," *Proceedings of the National Academy of Sciences of the United States of America,* 95 (1998), 7597–7602.

Than, Ker, "Ancient Fish Had Primitive Fingers, Toes," *National Geographic News* (September 24, 2008).

Thaxton, Charles B., Bradley, Walter L., and Olsen, Roger L., *The Mystery of Life's Origin,* Dallas: Lewis and Stanley, 1992.

Templeton, Alan R. ,"Human Origins and Analysis of Mitochondrial DNA Sequences," *Science,* 255 (1992), 737. Also footnote 22, 53.

Templeton, Alan R., "The 'Eve' Hypothesis: A Genetic Critique and Reanalysis," *American Anthropologist,* 95 (1), 1993, 52.

Thompson, Richard L., Cremo, Michael, and Gordon, Austin, *Origins,* Los Angeles: The Bhaktivedanta Book Trust, 1984, 26.

Tuttle, R. H., "Ape Footprints and Laetoli Impressions: A Response to the SUNY Claims," In Tobias, P. V., ed. *Hominid Evolution: Past, Present, and Future,* New York, Alan R. Liss, 1985, 129–133.

Utts, Jessica, and Josephson, Brian, "The Paranormal: The Evidence and Its Implications for Consciousness," from Times Higher Education Supplement's special section on Consciousness linked to the Tucson II conference "Toward a Science of Consciousness," Apr. 5, 1996, page v. Online at http://www.tcm.phy.cam.ac.uk/~bdj10/psi/tucson.html.

Van Lomme, Pim. "About the Continuity of Our Consciousness," *Advances in Experimental Medicine and Biology Adv Exp Med Biol.,* 550 (2004): 115–132. [Originally published in *Brain Death and Disorders of Consciousness.* Machado, C., and Shewmon, D. A., eds. New York, Boston, Dordrecht, London, Moscow: Kluwer Academic/ Plenum Publishers.] Available at the Internet (as of May 2008) at http://www.iands.org/research/important_studies/dr._pim_van_lommel_m.d._continuity_of_consciousness.html.

Vigilant, L., Stoneking, M., Harpending, H., Hawkes, K., and Wilson, A. C., "African Populations and the Evolution of Human Mitochondrial DNA," *Science,* 253 (1991), 1503–1507.

Wallace, Alfred R., *The Scientific Aspect of the Supernatural: Indicating the Desirableness of an Experimental Enquiry by Men of Science into the Alleged Powers of Clairvoyants and Mediums,* London: F. Farrah, 1866. Freely available on the Internet (as of May 2008) at: http://www.wku.edu/~smithch/wallace/S118A.htm.

Wallace, Alfred Russell, *Miracles and Modern Spiritualism.*, 3rd ed., London: George Redway, 1896.

Wallis, Claudia, "The Evolution Wars," *Time Magazine* (August 15, 2005), 27–35.

Webb, David, *Darwin's Secret Identity*, Sweden: Conch Press, 1985.

Wells, Jonathan, *Icons of Evolution*, Washington, DC: Regnery Publishing, 2002.

Wells, Jonathan, *The Politically Incorrect Guide to Darwinism and Intelligent Design*, Washington, DC: Regnery Publishing, 2006.

West, John G., *Darwin Day in America: How Our Politics and Culture Have Been Dehumanized in the Name of Science*, 1st ed., Wilmington, Delaware, USA: ISI Books, 2007.

Whitney, J. D., "The Auriferous Gravels of the Sierra Nevada of California," *Harvard University, Museum of Comparative Zoology Memoir* 6, 1 (1880).

Whitesides, George M., "Revolutions in Chemistry," *Chemical and Engineering News*, 85, 13 (March 26, 2007).

Wigner, Eugene P., "Two Kinds of Reality," *The Monist*, 48 (1964), 250.

Winchell, A., *Sparks from a Geologist's Hammer*, Chicago: S. C. Griggs, 1881.

Winslow, C. F., "The President Reads Extracts From a Letter from Dr. C. F. Winslow Relating the Discovery of Human Remains in Table Mountain, Cal. (Jan 1, 1873)," *Proceedings of the Boston Society of Natural History*, 15, 257–259.

Wilford, John Noble, "Fossil Called Missing Link From Sea to Land Animal," *New York Times* (April 6, 2006).

Wills, Christopher, *The Runaway Brain: The Evolution of Human Uniqueness*, New York, NY: Basic Books, 1993.

Woese, Carl, "The Universal Ancestor," *Proceedings of the National Academy of Sciences* USA, 95 (1998), 6854–6859.

Woese, Carl R., "A New Biology for a New Century," *Microbiology and Molecular Biology Reviews*, 68 (2004), 173–186.

Wolf, Yuri. I., et al., "Goelemata and Not Ecdysozoa: Evidence From Genome-Wide Phylogenetic Analysis," *Genome Research*, 14 (2004), 29–36.

Wood, B. A., "Evidence on the Locomotor Pattern of *Homo* from Early Pleistocene of Kenya," *Nature*, 251 (1974), 135–136.

Wong, Kate, "Newfound Fossil Is Transitional between Fish and Landlubbers," *Scientific American* (April 6, 2006). Online at http://www.sciam.com/article. cfm?id=newfound-fossil-is-transi.

Yonekura, K., Maki, S., Morgan, D. G., De Rosier, D. J., Vonderviszt, F., Imada, K., and Namba, K., "The Bacterial Flagellar Cap as the Rotary Promoter of Flagellin Self-assembly," *Science*, 290 (2000), 2148–2152.

About the Author

Danish science writer, Chairman of the Danish Society for Intelligent Design, and university lecturer on the subject of Darwinism and intelligent design, Leif Asmark Jensen has written numerous papers and articles exploring the convergence between modern science and traditional Eastern philosophy. He is associated with the Bhaktivedanta Institute and is the author of *Intelligent Design: et nyt syn på udviklingen* (*Intelligent Design: A New Look at Evolution*), the most popular book on intelligent design in Danish. He has also written a book on sustainable living and self-sufficient farming and is himself an active ecological farmer. Leif lives with his wife, Dorte, in Copenhagen, Denmark.